PSHE

FOR CCEA GCSE LEARNING FOR LIFE AND WORK

Kathryn Armstrong
Stephen Graham
Brigid McStravick

Hodder Murray
A MEMBER OF THE HODDER HEADLINE GROUP

p5l Rolf Bruderer/Corbis, r PA Photos; p6 British Nutrition Foundation 2003; p7t & b Rex Features; p11l Derek Cattani/Corbis, r Annie Griffiths Belt/Corbis; p15t Roy Morsch/Corbis, b Cordelia Molloy/Science Photo Library; p16t Science Photo Library, b Tek Image/Science Photo Library; p17t Tek Image/Science Photo Library, b Rex Features; p19 Rex Features; p21 Science Photo Library; p23 Rex Features; p26 Joseph Sohn/Corbis; p27 Wartenberg Picture Press/Corbis; p28; Royalty-Free/Corbis; p29 Franco Vogt/Corbis; p31t & b Rex Features; p33 Rex Features; p35 Royalty-Free/Corbis; p36l Tim Kiusalaas/Corbis, r Mark Peterson/Corbis; p40 Royalty-Free/Corbis; p44 Rex Features; p46l Matthew Klein/Corbis, m Edifice/Corbis, t courtesy of Alfa Romeo , b Royalty-Free/Corbis; p49 Bob Krist/Corbis; p50t&b Peter Keogh; p52 BDI Images Ltd; p59 James W Porter/Corbis; p61t Yang Liu/Corbis, m courtesy of Fiat, b Toshiba; p62 Edifice/Corbis; p65 Peter Keogh.

In this book, we have, to the best of our knowledge, described the law as it stood in July 2004. However, in trying to summarise and simplify the law we have had to leave out some legal details. Therefore, this book cannot be taken as proof of your legal rights. It will be important in some circumstances to seek further advice before taking any action.

Note about the Internet links in the book. The user should be aware that URLs or web addresses change regularly. Every effort has been made to ensure the accuracy of the URLs provided in this book on going to press. It is inevitable, however, that some will change. It is sometimes possible to find a relocated web page, by just typing in the address of the home page for a website in the URL window of your browser.

Orders: please contact Bookpoint Ltd, 130 Milton Park, Abingdon, Oxon OX14 4SB. Telephone: (44) 01235 827720. Fax: (44) 01235 400454. Lines are open from 9.00 - 6.00, Monday to Saturday, with a 24 hour message answering service. You can also order through our website www.hodderheadline.co.uk

British Library Cataloguing in Publication Data
A catalogue record for this title is available from the British Library

ISBN-10: 0 340 86916 X
ISBN-13: 978 0 340 86916 1

First Published 2004
Impression number 10 9 8 7 6 5 4 3
Year 2010 2009 2008 2007 2006 2005

Cover photo from gettyimages/Photographer Jacques Copeau
Typeset by Black Dog Design. Artwork by Steve Parkhouse at Daedalus Studios.
Printed in Italy for Hodder Murray, an imprint of Hodder Education, a member of the Hodder Headline Group, 338 Euston Road, London NW1 3BH

Contents

1. Pressures and influences

Aims

At the end of this unit you should be able to:

- identify some of the pressures and influences on young people
- develop strategies to manage these pressures and influences.

As you are growing up there will be different pressures and influences on you: from your peers, parents and teachers, regarding your attitudes, values and beliefs, future choices (e.g., what you decide to do after you leave school) and how you look and behave. Some of the ways in which to manage and cope with these pressures are outlined in this unit.

Values and beliefs

As you grow older you will find you have a stronger sense of things you value and believe in. For example, you develop a definite sense of right and wrong, justice and injustice. You may form stronger political or religious views.

Your values and beliefs are important as they help establish who you are. You can sometimes feel pressured if your values or beliefs are different from those around you. This means you may have some difficult choices to make.

What would you do in this situation?

activity

What happens if your values or beliefs put you in direct conflict with a friend who has different values or beliefs to you? Do you let them influence or pressure you?

Imagine the following situation:

Your friends are involved in underage drinking and are putting pressure on you to join in, even though you do not agree with it. Despite telling them the obvious consequences of underage drinking, they try to convince you that it is only a bit of harmless fun.

What do you do? Do you turn your back on them, or do you accept that they have a right to their views and opinions? Do you compromise in some way? You may have to decide whether it is worth losing your friendship with the group, changing your values or beliefs, or accepting you have different views.

Some strategies to help deal with peer pressure

1. **Ignore what is going on and try not to let it affect or influence you.**
2. **Walk away from a situation which makes you feel uncomfortable.**
3. **Try to discourage the activity.**
4. **Be confrontational, but remember that this may compromise your friendship.**
5. **Seek advice from a more experienced person (e.g., another friend, a teacher or parent).**

activity

A new pupil arrives in your class. She is quiet and seems unsure of herself. Your friends decide it would be 'a laugh' to pick on her and give her a hard time in the class. You know this is wrong.

- What do you say to your friends?
- Do you just go along with them because you are afraid they will pick on you too?
- Do you ignore all of them and hope the situation does not get out of hand?
- What does your choice tell you about your **personality**?
- Re-create this situation through role play in a group.

Future choices

Another pressure that you may experience is choosing what you want to do when you leave school. Do you want to get a job, an apprenticeship, or go to university, etc.? Your parents or teachers may be putting pressure on you to choose one option rather than another. It may be that you find yourself changing your mind a number of times as you develop your ambitions and goals for the future. What you like or dislike, or what subjects you are good at or not good at, may influence you. However, thinking about what you would like to achieve is very useful and helps you develop your sense of identity.

How people see you

By now you already have a well-defined **self-image**. However, you now have to choose how other people see you. There is the expression 'first impressions count'. People get an impression of you based mainly on two things: the way you behave and the way you look. You may already be aware that you judge people on these two things, so you should also be aware that people judge you in the same way.

There are a lot of pressures placed on you to make you dress or behave in certain ways:

- Other people put you under pressure (e.g., parents, teachers, friends, pop stars, etc.).
- The **media** puts you under pressure (through advertising on television and in magazines and newspapers).

It is important to be aware of these pressures when deciding on the image you want to present to others.

Managing these pressures can be difficult. For example, being part of a crowd can often mean 'looking' or 'acting' like the rest of the group. To deal with this you need to decide what is right for you and ask yourself questions such as: Can I afford that look? When I am older will that tattoo or piercing be appropriate? You then need to have the strength to say no.

If someone tries to pressurise you into acting, behaving or dressing in a way that makes you feel uncomfortable, they are possibly not as good a friend as you thought.

Do you judge these people differently because of the way they look?

activities

1. Imagine that you are interviewing candidates for a job which involves regularly meeting clients. List five things that are important for the candidate to have in order to get the job (leaving out qualifications), and five things that would prevent the candidate from getting the job.
2. Write down how you see yourself today in terms of your values and beliefs, your identity and your goals. Now repeat the task, this time imagining yourself in ten years' time.
3. Imagine that you are out with your friends, one of whom has just passed their driving test. While celebrating at a local nightclub you see your friend, who will be driving home, drink alcohol. What strategies would you try in order to deal with this situation?

2. A healthy lifestyle

Aims

At the end of this unit you should be able to:

- understand what the term **health** means
- realise the importance of a **balanced diet**
- understand how your lifestyle can affect your health.

Some definitions of health

The World Health Organisation (WHO) defines health as 'a complete state of physical, mental and social wellbeing and not simply the absence of disease or infirmity'.

Health can also be defined as a sense of wellbeing, both physical and emotional, brought about by positive lifestyle choices.

There are different forms of health:

- physical health includes **diet**, nutrition and exercise
- emotional or **mental health** includes self-confidence, emotions and dealing with stress.

In this unit, the focus will be on diet and nutrition and how they contribute to a healthy lifestyle.

A balanced diet?

A balanced diet means eating different food types in the right proportions so that your body gets the variety of substances it needs to maintain it. It is important that the amount of energy you get from the food you eat is equal to the amount of energy you use up on a daily basis. If you eat too much food then the energy is not all used and is stored as fat. If you do not eat enough food then you do not produce enough energy and you end up feeling tired and listless. This is why it is important to have a balanced diet.

In Northern Ireland, many people are not as fit and healthy as they could be because of their lifestyles. Some people do not eat the correct foods or eat too much of a particular food (such as fried food), or too little of another (such as fruit and vegetables). This means they do not have a balanced diet.

Having a balanced diet also includes eating at regular times; it is recommended that we eat three meals each day.

Your nutritional needs depend on your age. **Adolescents** require a greater intake of protein for growth and carbohydrate for energy, as opposed to an elderly person whose body is fully developed and who is less active.

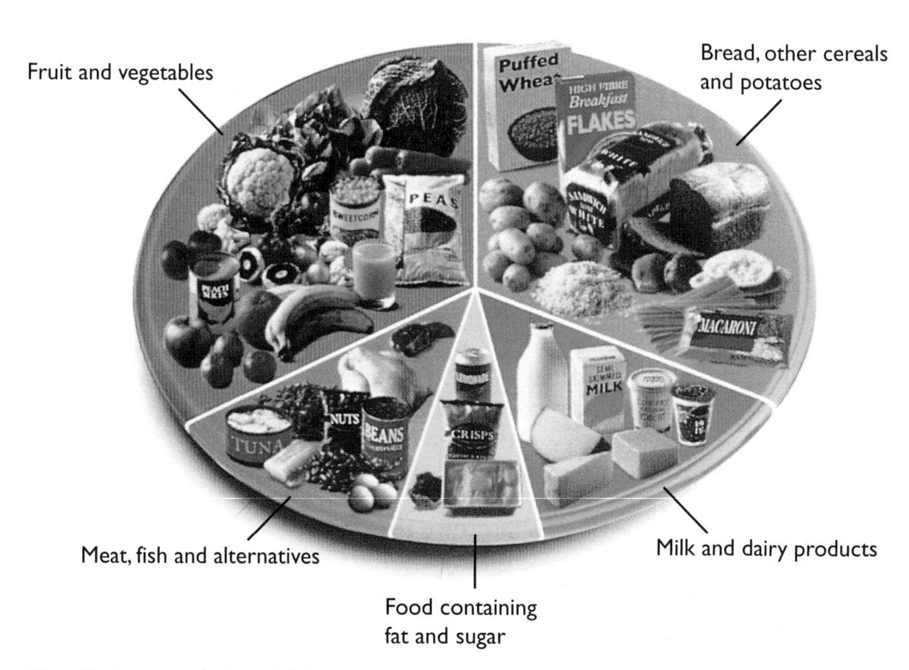

The Balance of Good Health. This diagram shows what proportion of different food types you should eat.

Getting the balance right

Because no single food contains all the nutrients needed to provide a balanced diet, we need to eat a variety of foods. Poor food choices can result in ill health and nutritional disorders. If you make the right choices you can enjoy a balanced diet, look good and feel well. You should:

- eat a wide variety of foods
- eat the right amount of food
- eat plenty of foods that are high in fibre and starch
- reduce the amount of fat you eat (some fats can be hidden so read labels carefully)
- not eat sugary foods too often
- look after the vitamins in food (processing food can destroy them)
- enjoy eating your food by not rushing meals
- eat at regular times.

Health risks

If you lead a lifestyle where you smoke, drink a lot of alcohol, eat a lot of fatty foods and do little exercise you run the risk of the following:

Cardiovascular disease (CVD)

This affects more men than women and kills one in three people in the form of heart attacks and **angina**. By making small changes in your diet (e.g., reducing the proportion of saturated fat, animal fat, and increasing the amount of fruit, vegetables, wholegrain and fibre) you can reduce the risk of CVD.

Obesity

This is when a person is 20% over the recommended weight for their height and build. Obesity is caused by a number of factors including genes, lack of physical activity and eating foods high in energy (calories). This can be avoided by reducing the amount of fat in your diet and by incorporating an exercise programme into your daily or weekly routine.

Type 2 diabetes

This is usually associated with poor diet or old age and can be controlled by diet.

Eating disorders

An abnormal attitude to food can cause you to either eat too much or too little and put you at risk of developing:

- Anorexia nervosa, an eating disorder characterised by self-inflicted starvation that results in extreme weight loss.
- Bulimia, an eating disorder characterised by the consumption of large amounts of high calorie foods (bingeing) followed by self-induced vomiting.

activity

- Write down a list of the food you would normally eat each day of the week.
- Change some of the food items to make your list more healthy but still enjoyable – remember it is possible to enjoy food and be more healthy.
- Now try out the new menu and record the results and any comments you have.

A lifestyle where you have an abnormal attitude towards food can lead to health problems.

3. Exercise and the body

Aims

At the end of this unit you should be able to:

- define **fitness**
- understand the short- and long-term effects of physical exercise
- develop an individual programme of healthy exercise.

Exercise, like a balanced diet, is important in a healthy lifestyle. It keeps you fit and able to cope with the demands of everyday life.

What is fitness?

Fitness can be broken down into a number of areas:

1. Cardiovascular endurance is the ability of the cardiovascular system (heart, blood, lungs) to deliver oxygen as required to the muscles. This is called aerobic fitness.
2. Muscular endurance is the ability of the muscles to repeat a movement or action or activity without tiring.
3. Stamina is the ability to keep on going for long periods of time without tiring (a combination of cardiovascular and muscular endurance).
4. Strength is the force a muscle exerts when it contracts.
5. Flexibility is the range of movement at a joint.
6. Speed is the ability to move your body or part of your body quickly.
7. Body composition is the ratio between the amount of fat and lean tissues in your body (this is linked to diet). Too much fat or too little fat can mean you are unfit.

In order to cope with the normal demands of life you will need the minimum level of fitness in each of these areas. If the demands increase then the level of fitness required will be greater. Athletes need a high level of fitness in all or most of these areas.

The benefits of physical exercise

Regular exercise helps keep us fit and has both short- and long-term benefits.

Short-term benefits

- Physical activity is stimulating and fun.
- Physical activity helps get rid of stress and aggression in a harmless way.
- Physical activity can prevent boredom, as it can stimulate and provide a challenge.
- You will sleep much better after physical activity, so you will be more rested the next day.

Long-term benefits

Physical benefits:

- You will look and feel better.
- You won't tire as easily.
- Your muscles will get stronger and more efficient.
- Your posture will improve, because you will have stronger back and stomach muscles.
- You will have less body fat, as it will get burned up.
- Your joints will become more flexible.
- Your bones will get stronger.

Mental benefits:

- Success in a physical activity will boost your self-esteem.
- Physical activity can help to reduce tiredness.
- Physical activity can help to improve concentration.

Social benefits:

- Participating in a team activity means you will meet more people and sometimes make new friends.
- You will learn new skills (e.g., team work and co-operation) that are useful in other aspects of life.
- A feeling of belonging to a group.

Factors affecting fitness

Being fit also means being healthy, and there are a number of factors that affect this:

Age	You generally are at your fittest in your twenties.
Gender	From 11 years old, boys tend to grow stronger and taller than girls; however, girls usually grow more flexible.
Build	Your build will affect the type of exercise you are more suited to (e.g., compare the build of a weightlifter to that of a gymnast or a swimmer).
Diet	A healthy well-balanced diet is important when it comes to fitness.
Exercise	This is a very important factor and, no matter what your age, regular exercise will keep you fit.
Physical disabilities	These may prevent you from taking part in some physical activities but you can still participate in others to stay fit.
Illness	This can affect your fitness and health on a short- or long-term basis, so it is important to have sufficient rest during and immediately after an illness.
Taking drugs	Drugs can affect your physical and mental health levels, so they should be avoided unless necessary (e.g., prescribed medication).
Stress	This can affect your mental and physical fitness levels; however, exercise is a good way to relieve stress.
Environment	This can affect both your health and fitness levels (e.g., inner-city pollution can damage your lungs and affect your ability to exercise).

Push–pull factors

Knowing the benefits of taking part in a sport or physical recreation, you would think that everyone would get involved in some form of exercise; however, there is a trend (which is increasing) for young people not to participate. Why is this? There are a number of reasons:

Age	As you get older you are less likely to exercise or continue to exercise.
Gender	Fewer females tend to exercise than males.
School	Unless your school has a strong sporting tradition or programme you are less likely to get involved.
Family	Unless you are encouraged by parents you are less likely to participate in sports. Young people may also depend on parents to provide money, equipment or transport.
Peer group pressure	If your peer group do not participate in a physical activity, or if they openly disapprove of physical activity, you may be less likely to participate.
Facilities	Unless there are good sport and recreation facilities close to where you live you are less likely to get involved in sports.
Disability	This may restrict your choice of exercise.
Economics	Some activities are expensive (e.g., golf), so it may be more difficult for you to take part in them.
The media	This can influence participation in some sports (e.g., more people take up tennis during and immediately after Wimbledon fortnight than at any other time of the year). However, it can also encourage us to merely watch instead of taking part.

activity

- In small groups, design a six-week fitness programme aimed at increasing your fitness levels. Things that must be taken into consideration are your current fitness levels, your likes/dislikes about exercise, any health problems, facilities near you, whether it is a group activity, etc.
- Keep a record of your fitness programme. How many times a week do you take part and how long for? Are there any physical benefits (pulse rate, ease of performance, increase or decrease in weight, etc.)?

4. Mental health

Aims

At the end of this unit you should be able to:

- define mental health
- understand the factors affecting mental health
- understand the effects of pressures on mental health.

When we think about being healthy we tend to think about it in terms of being physically healthy. Mental health is sometimes not considered, or even ignored altogether. However, our mental well-being is just as important as our physical wellbeing as it affects our ability to function to the best of our ability.

Mental health is our ability to cope with stress and our ability to control our emotions. It affects our ability to enjoy ourselves and our feelings of self-confidence and self-worth.

What is mental illness?

Mental illness is a term that is used to describe a range of illnesses that affect the mind. The effects of mental illness usually include feelings of **depression**, **anxiety** and **confusion**. When a person is suffering from a mental illness their feelings make it hard for them to cope with everyday life in a way that they previously perceived as 'normal'. They experience these feelings strongly and over a long period of time.

The good news is that mental illness is often only a temporary condition. It can be treated through talking to therapists/psychiatrists or, in some cases, through courses of prescribed medication.

Because of the consequences of modern-day society, with its increasingly stressful way of life, mental illness is more common than it used to be. About 15% of people will experience a form of mental illness at some time in their life.

People who suffer from mental illness often ignore the problem, or won't admit to it, as they feel that others around them will see them as weak or unable to cope. This means that treatment of the illness can often take longer than it could have done, because, by the time the person accepts there is something wrong, the problem has had longer to develop.

In the past, people who had a mental health problem were seen as 'mad', violent or possessed by an evil spirit. This view, even today, still affects the sufferer when it comes to admitting that there is a problem.

Causes

Mental ill health or illness is often caused by a combination of stresses and pressures which can be broken down into four main causes:

1. Physical causes

Illness Quite often after a physical illness, an accident or an operation, a person can feel 'down' or depressed (e.g., post-natal depression, or feeling low after a severe bout of flu).

Drug misuse People who misuse drugs often suffer from mood swings and can even feel suicidal. Some drugs alter the chemical balance of the brain and that, in turn, can lead to depression and, in later life, **dementia**. Drug dependency can have a negative effect on your way of life (e.g., reduced income, physical illness, failure at school, loss of friends, etc.), which can increase stress.

2. Inherited factors

People with a history of mental illness in their family tend to be more likely to have mental health problems.

3. Social causes

Home life Stress from problems at home is one of the most common causes of mental ill health. Young people who come from family backgrounds where they feel insecure because of relationship problems, money problems, or a family break-up, etc., tend to be more prone to suffering from mental illness than young people from secure family backgrounds.

Pressure to succeed Pressure from others to succeed often creates feelings in people of being unable to cope or compete, which causes stress. This can lead to depression and low self-esteem which, in turn, can reduce their ability to succeed; pressure to succeed can, therefore, be the start of a downward spiral.

We often measure success by material things (e.g., by having an expensive car, a house and a job). If a person feels unable to achieve these things then they can start to see themselves as unsuccessful or a failure. This lowers self-esteem and can lead to mental illness.

Worrying about losing a job, or not getting a job, can be very stressful, which can affect a person's feeling of self-worth. (Suicide rates always climb during times of high unemployment and reduce during times of high employment.)

4. Environmental causes

Living environment A person is more likely to suffer from mental ill health if they live in a large city than if they live in a small town. This is possibly due to the overcrowding, poor housing, loneliness and much faster pace of life of the large cities.

Work environment The workplace can also affect a person's mental health. Jobs that are particularly demanding, with long working hours, cause stress. Also, travelling a long distance to and from work can reduce rest time and increase stress. As already noted, high levels of stress can lead to mental ill health.

activities

1. Try to list the pressures that you feel affect you the most (e.g., relationships, exams, etc.). Write down how you feel at these 'stressful' times and what you do to cope with the situation.
2. Read through a variety of young people's magazines and identify the pressures they put on you and your peers. Discuss your findings with the class.

Where you live can affect your mental health.

5. Legal substances

Aims

At the end of this unit you should be able to:

- define what a drug is and what drug misuse is
- develop a knowledge of legal substances and their effects
- understand the health risks of taking legal substances.

Definitions

A drug is a chemical substance that is used for its ability to alter the physical, mental and emotional state of the user.

Drug misuse (*abuse*) is the non-medical use of a drug to achieve the experience of some altered state of consciousness.

There are a number of drugs that are classified as legal. However, when something is 'legal' it is generally thought to be 'safe'. This is not true where drugs are concerned, as all drugs could potentially cause harm or death. For example, paracetamol, used as a painkiller, can kill if too many are taken.

The table below and opposite describes some common legal substances, their effects, and the risks involved in taking them.

activity

Many young people smoke and/or drink alcohol when they are underage. These people are at increased risk of causing damage to themselves through accidents or disease. In small groups, discuss why young people ignore the risks of smoking and drinking, despite the current awareness campaigns.

Drug	Description	Effects	Risks	Legal Status
Alcohol	• Drink, such as beer, wine and spirits. • Seen as a safe drug because it can be bought over the counter and is generally socially acceptable.	• Taken in moderation, this can sometimes make the user relaxed, sociable or aggressive. • Slurred speech. • Depressant. • Working on the central nervous system, it affects co-ordination, reaction time and the ability to perform tasks properly. • Hangover: headache and illness caused by alcohol abuse the previous day/night. • The effects vary with individuals depending on: – their weight – whether they have eaten – their mood – the strength of the drink – how much they consumed and how fast – their gender (men can generally consume more than women because of the difference in body mass).	• Depression: alcohol can intensify feelings, so someone who is already feeling 'down' can become more depressed through alcohol use. • Overdose can lead to unconsciousness, coma or death from choking on your own vomit. • Linked to 25,000 deaths each year. • Sustained overuse can lead to damage to the liver, heart, stomach and brain. • Addiction.	Legal to sell to people over the age of 18.

Drug	Description	Effects	Risks	Legal Status
Nicotine	• Pre-made cigarettes and loose tobacco. • Nicotine is the drug in tobacco. • Tobacco also contains other substances such as tar and carbon monoxide which are harmful to your health.	• Mild stimulant: it speeds up the heart rate and increases blood pressure. • First-time users may feel sick. • Users have the smell of tobacco on their breath, hair and clothes and often have nicotine stains on their fingers and teeth. • Sense of taste and smell become less effective.	• Very addictive, both psychologically and physically. • Associated with heart disease, causing fatty deposits to build up in the arteries. • Causes cancer (e.g., lung and throat cancer). • Circulation problems: responsible for 2,000 limb amputations each year. • Responsible for 125,000 premature deaths each year.	Legal to sell to people over the age of 16.
Volatile substances (solvents)	• Fast-drying glues and adhesives, assorted paint and petroleum products, lighter fluid, dry-cleaning fluids, assorted aerosol sprays, surgical spirit, cleaners, etc. • Solvent abuse involves inhaling the fumes from domestic and industrial products creating a strong intoxication. • The most common method of inhaling solvents is from a plastic bag which is placed over the face.	• Thick-headed, dreamy, dizzy and giggly. • Causes **hallucinations**. • Effects last up to 5 minutes. • Headaches, sleepiness and sickness after use.	• Death: 50% of first-time users die through suffocation – both from vomiting and if the bag used sticks to the mouth or nose. • Reckless acts leading to accidents. • Liver, heart, kidney and brain damage.	Illegal to sell to people under the age of 16.
Poppers	• Liquid amyl nitrite and butyl nitrite. • Street names include: Rush, Ram and TNT.	• Causes dilation of blood vessels leading to the heart, accompanied by decrease in blood pressure and increase in heart rate. This causes a brief, intense surge of blood through the heart and brain – causing a rush. • Effect lasts 2–5 minutes. • Faintness and sickness. • Headache during and after use. • Acne around the nose and mouth.	• Heart and blood pressure problems. • Death can occur if the drug is swallowed.	• Butyl nitrite is not classified; it can therefore be bought over the counter. • Amyl nitrite must be prescribed by a doctor.
Magic mushrooms	• Varieties of mushrooms found growing in the wild.	• Similar hallucinogenic effect to LSD (see page 16). • Effects last 4–8 hours. • Alters the user's mood, senses and perception (i.e., sound, speech, distance, colour, vision, etc.). • Damages short-term memory. • Stomach pains, cramp and diarrhoea.	• The effect of altered perception puts the user at risk of physical and mental injury. • 'Bad trips' can lead to 4–8 hours of fear. • Eating the wrong type of mushroom can lead to death through poisoning.	Not illegal to pick, but illegal to process (i.e., dry or cook).

6. Illegal substances

Aims

At the end of this unit you should be able to:

- know the classification of drugs
- understand the effects of different illegal substances
- understand the health risks of different illegal substances.

Classification

In the UK, illegal drugs are divided into three main classes: A, B and C, with Class A drugs having the most serious punishments for possession and drug-trafficking.

Class A

These include amphetamines (speed) when prepared for injection, heroin, cocaine, ecstasy and LSD. Possession of a Class A drug has a maximum prison sentence of seven years. Trafficking a Class A drug can lead to life imprisonment.

Class B

These include amphetamines (speed) if not prepared for injection, and barbiturates. Possession of a Class B drug can lead to five years' imprisonment, whereas trafficking has a maximum penalty of 14 years' imprisonment.

Class C

These include mild amphetamines (such as diet pills), steroids and cannabis (since 2004). For possession, the maximum penalty is two years' imprisonment. Trafficking Class C drugs can lead to a maximum prison sentence of 14 years.

Quality

As well as the risks associated with individual drugs (see pages 15–17) there is also the added risk that, because these drugs are illegal, there is no quality control involved in their production; drug purity cannot, therefore, be guaranteed.

The drugs are often 'cut' (i.e., diluted with other substances to make up the bulk of the tablet, capsule or liquid) with a variety of substances that the buyer is unaware of. These have included: brick dust, dog worming tablets, sawdust, Vim (powder bleach), rat poison and talcum powder. Plaster of Paris has been found in heroin that is used for injecting.

activity

Classifying drugs as A, B and C can create the impression that Class C drugs, such as cannabis, are safer than Class A drugs, such as heroin. Is this necessarily the case?

Study one drug from each class and look at its risks from the point of view of:

– how it is taken
– the physical and mental risks to the user.

Types of drug

Cannabis	
Street names	Blow, draw, pot, hash, grass, wacky-backy, dope.
What it is	The most commonly found form is resin. Herbal (the dried leaf) would be the next most common form. It is a Class C drug. It is smoked (usually with tobacco) or eaten.
Effects	The user feels talkative and relaxed; they experience a heightened sense of taste, colour and sound (often with an increased appetite). The user later feels tired, depressed and restless.
Risks	The drug affects the short-term memory, making it difficult to recall information (students beware!). Causes concentration and co-ordination problems. Causes respiratory problems (one 'joint' is equal to six normal cigarettes), including bronchitis and lung cancer. Girls who smoke cannabis are ten times more likely to have a child born with leukaemia. It is linked to infertility and impotence in males. There is risk of psychological **dependence** as well as psychological disturbances, such as paranoia and anxiety, with excessive use.

Amphetamines	
Street names	Speed, Billy Wizzy, whizzy, uppers.
What it is	These are stimulants. They can be snorted, swallowed, injected or dissolved in a drink. The drug name is amphetamine sulphate and was originally prescribed for extreme over-activity, a pathological tendency to fall asleep (narcolepsy), or as an appetite suppressant (diet pills). They are Class B drugs unless they are prepared for injection (when they become Class A).
Effects	An increase in breathing rate and heart rate. The user feels confident and energetic. Causes the user to need little or no sleep for two or three days. Appetite suppressant. Can cause the user to feel tense or anxious.
Risks	Coming 'down' from the drug can last for about two days (depending on the amount used). **Tolerance** to the drug develops. Sleep, memory and concentration are affected. Because of the 'feel good' effect of the drug, the user can develop psychological dependence. Heart failure is possible in heavy, prolonged use. Ill health because of lack of sleep and food intake. After use, the individual becomes very tired and depressed, which can lead to further use of the drug to deal with the **withdrawal** effects.

Ecstasy	
Street names	'E', XTC, Dennis the Menace, or the brand name given by the logo on the tablet (e.g., Doves, 007, Mitsubishi, etc.).
What it is	This drug is a stimulant. It is a Class A drug that is swallowed, sniffed or injected. There is no medical use for this drug but it is frequently attributed to the 'rave' scene. The proper name for ecstasy is methylenedioxymethylamphetamine (MDMA).
Effects	The user feels alert and energetic. The user experiences an increase in perception (sound, colour, etc.). Emotions are more intense (commonly called being 'loved up'). Insomnia. Increase in body temperature, sweating and dehydration. Tightening of the jaw. Mood swings.
Risks	Increased breathing rate and heart rate, leading to high blood pressure. Liver and kidney problems. Prevents the body getting rid of water. Ingested fluids are reabsorbed by the brain, in particular, which can swell and crush itself against the skull, causing death. Blood clots can develop in the lungs.

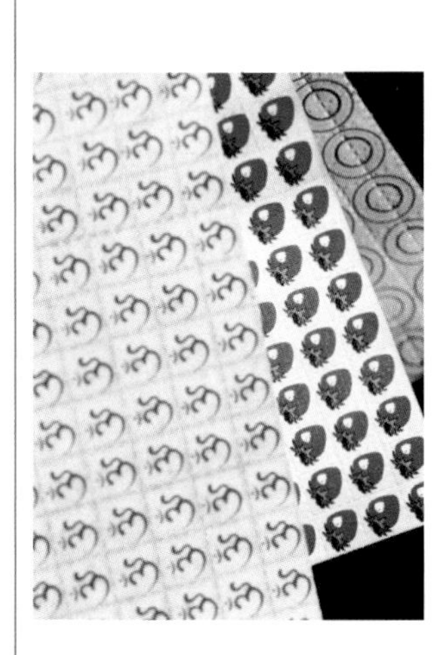

LSD	
Street names	Acid, acid-tabs, trips, or related to the logo on the tab (e.g., strawberry, smiley faces, moon phase, Bart Simpson, etc.).
What it is	It is a Class A, hallucinogenic drug. It is eaten as tiny pills or as transfers on blotting paper. The proper name for LSD is lysergic acid diethylamide.
Effects	The drug alters the user's perceptions (e.g., speed, distance, colour and hearing). The user hallucinates. The effects of one 'trip' last 8–12 hours; if it is a 'bad trip' this can be terrifying. The drug affects the user's mood. However, just because the user is in a good mood it does not mean they will experience a 'good trip'.
Risks	'Trips' are unpredictable. A bad 'trip' can be terrifying. Tolerance quickly develops. Can cause feelings of paranoia and of being 'out of control'. 'Flashbacks' can occur up to 15 years after stopping use. Can lead to mental and emotional problems. Suicide and accidental deaths have occurred through use of this drug. Psychological dependence can develop.

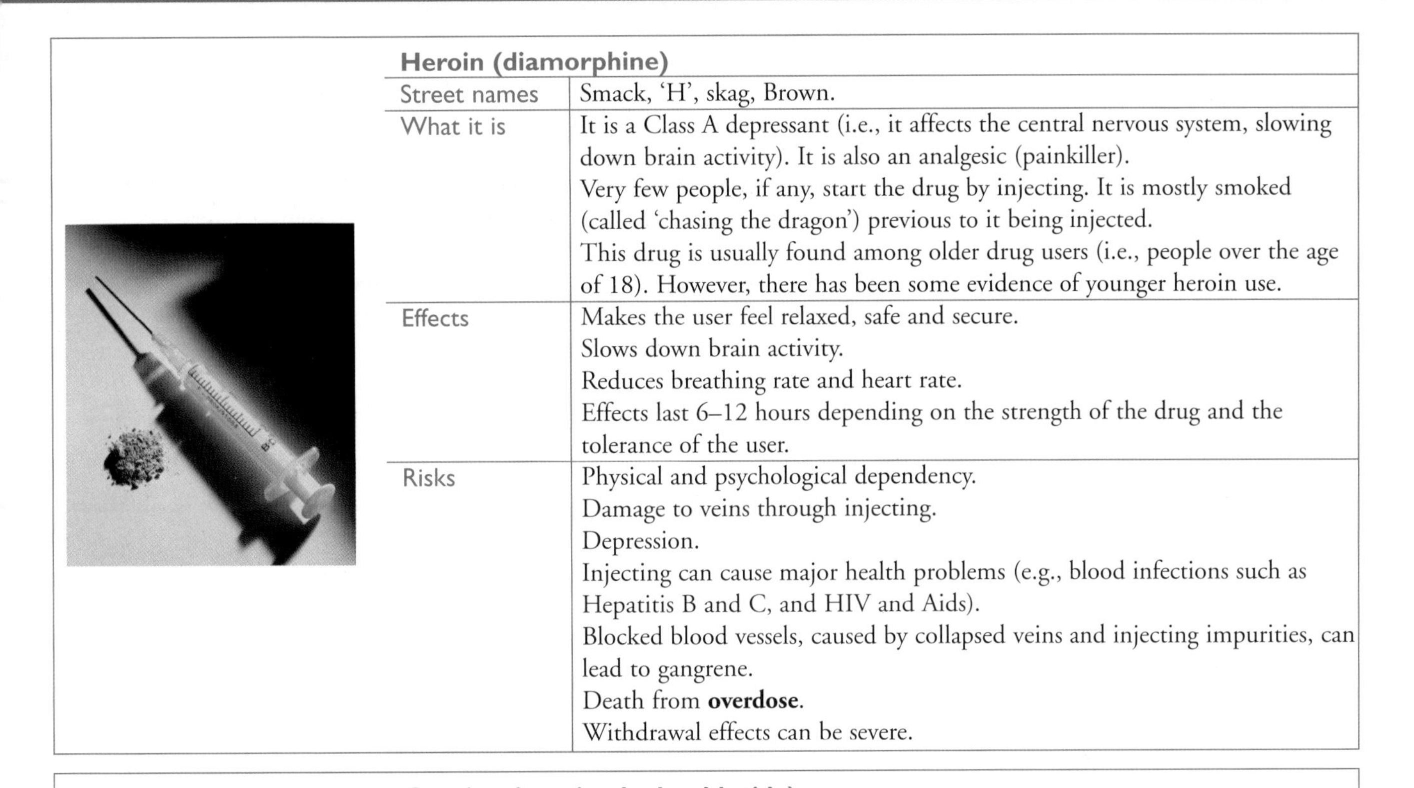

Heroin (diamorphine)	
Street names	Smack, 'H', skag, Brown.
What it is	It is a Class A depressant (i.e., it affects the central nervous system, slowing down brain activity). It is also an analgesic (painkiller). Very few people, if any, start the drug by injecting. It is mostly smoked (called 'chasing the dragon') previous to it being injected. This drug is usually found among older drug users (i.e., people over the age of 18). However, there has been some evidence of younger heroin use.
Effects	Makes the user feel relaxed, safe and secure. Slows down brain activity. Reduces breathing rate and heart rate. Effects last 6–12 hours depending on the strength of the drug and the tolerance of the user.
Risks	Physical and psychological dependency. Damage to veins through injecting. Depression. Injecting can cause major health problems (e.g., blood infections such as Hepatitis B and C, and HIV and Aids). Blocked blood vessels, caused by collapsed veins and injecting impurities, can lead to gangrene. Death from **overdose**. Withdrawal effects can be severe.

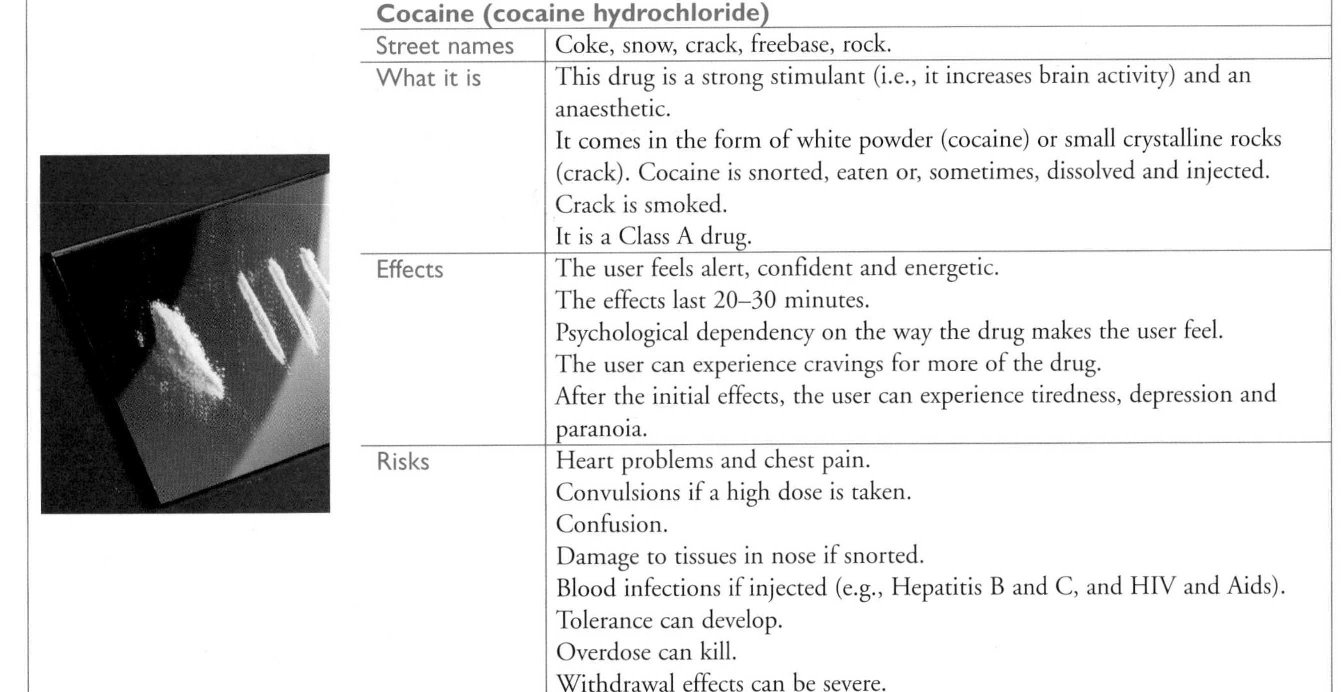

Cocaine (cocaine hydrochloride)	
Street names	Coke, snow, crack, freebase, rock.
What it is	This drug is a strong stimulant (i.e., it increases brain activity) and an anaesthetic. It comes in the form of white powder (cocaine) or small crystalline rocks (crack). Cocaine is snorted, eaten or, sometimes, dissolved and injected. Crack is smoked. It is a Class A drug.
Effects	The user feels alert, confident and energetic. The effects last 20–30 minutes. Psychological dependency on the way the drug makes the user feel. The user can experience cravings for more of the drug. After the initial effects, the user can experience tiredness, depression and paranoia.
Risks	Heart problems and chest pain. Convulsions if a high dose is taken. Confusion. Damage to tissues in nose if snorted. Blood infections if injected (e.g., Hepatitis B and C, and HIV and Aids). Tolerance can develop. Overdose can kill. Withdrawal effects can be severe.

activity

Copy and complete this table (right) and add an entry for all 11 drug types mentioned in units 5 and 6 of this section (pages 12–17). The first one is completed for you.

Drug name	An effect	A risk	Legal status
Solvents	*Dizzy*	*Suffocation*	*Legal substance, but illegal to sell to people under the age of 16.*

7. Drug use

Aims

At the end of this unit you should be able to:

- understand the key factors in drug use
- understand the different levels of drug use
- realise the consequences of drug use.

Key factors

It is important to realise that drug use among young people is not always simply a case of doing it for fun or curiosity. There are three main factors which contribute to a young person becoming involved in drugs and continuing to use drugs in their late teens and beyond:

1. The individual

This takes into account the personality of the young person. For example, are they easily led, a loner or a risk-taker?

What is their family background, physical health, weight, gender (sex)?

2. The situation

Is it the first time that he/she has considered using drugs?

Does **peer pressure** or social drug use (i.e., with friends) play a role?

Where is the drug used (e.g., a club, outside, etc.) and what is the person doing (e.g., driving)?

3. The drug

Is the drug used because it is widely available, because there is nothing else available, or because it is cheap?

Is the drug used for its effect (upper/downer, hallucinogenic, or causes the user feel calm, 'buzzy', etc.)?

The effect of the drug is an important factor for some young people who are experienced in drug use. For example, if a user is going to a nightclub he/she might choose to take ecstasy, as it provides the energy required to dance for long periods. Cannabis is used for its calming effect, alcohol is perceived as a social drug, and LSD and magic mushrooms are used for their hallucinogenic, or 'trippy', effect.

For an inexperienced user, the effect of the drug might not be as important a factor, as he/she is more likely to be buying the drug to 'find out' (i.e., out of curiosity or as an experiment).

Ecstasy gives the user energy.

activities

1. Using the three key factors that contribute to drug use, state how you could help prevent a young person from becoming involved in drug use.
2. Below are three individuals in situations where they are going to use a drug. Work out which drug they would choose and explain why.

Boy 1 has been invited to a rave.

Girl 1 is meeting some friends for a party.

Boy 2 is looking for a new 'trippy' experience.

Levels of drug use

When considering drug use among young people it is important to understand the four levels of drug use:

Level 1 – experimental use

This is often seen as being a short-term group activity. The drug taken and the way it is taken is influenced by how available a drug is, the company of the drug user, where it is taken and current trends (what is fashionable). The pattern of drug use is irregular and the purpose is to 'find out' about the effects.

Experimental use is also called 'novice use' and carries its own risks based on the lack of knowledge about the drug and its effects. For example: 50% of first-time solvent users die through suffocation; people have become very ill, or have died, from picking the wrong type of mushrooms when attempting to use magic mushrooms; the mind-altering effect of LSD can affect the user's perceptions, which can lead to injury or death.

Level 2 – recreational use

The key factor here is enjoyment. The young person using the drug feels that he/she has acquired control over the drug in terms of the kind of drug used and where or when it is taken. Recreational use ranges from occasional to heavy use, but where the user is not dependent on the drug. Here, the young person chooses a drug based on how it makes them feel or what they intend to do.

This use is often seen as part of 'normal' teenage social culture. However, the danger here is the user's complacency about taking an illegal drug: 'I've done it before and I was fine, therefore it must be safe to do it again!'

Level 3 – dependent use

This type of use is more likely to be a long-term activity. With dependent use there is either a physical or psychological desire to use the drug. At this stage the user has lost control of their drug use.

People who are dependent tend to use large amounts of the drug and more often. Getting the drug becomes more important than the quality of the drug or the satisfaction of the experience.

This type of use is usually a small group activity, or a solitary practice, and is linked to emotional, psychological and social problems such as:

- crime to pay for the drugs
- lack of interest in personal appearance
- poor health
- school or family problems.

Level 4 – problem use

This type of drug use can occur at any stage. In other words, it is not linked to the amount or frequency of use. An example of this would be the effect on a community where young people are drinking in the street and creating problems for residents. Another example would be a first-time solvent abuser who dies.

What problems might these teenagers cause for the local community?

activities

1. Compare and contrast any two of the four levels of drug use. For example, imagine one person who is experimenting with drugs and another person who is dependent on a drug. What differences would there be between their lifestyles?
2. What are the physical, social and emotional consequences of each of the four levels of drug use?
3. Using the Internet, research the two types of drug addiction: physical and psychological. Using the information found, prepare a discussion paper (for a maximum two minutes) for your class.

8. Substance misuse

Aims

At the end of this unit you should be able to:

- understand the pressures and influences leading to drug misuse.

It is now widely believed that there is no reason for a young person to become involved in illicit or illegal drug use. When we talk about, or refer to, the reasons why young people misuse substances we should talk in terms of pressures and influences.

Pressures and influences explained

Fun or enjoyment (hedonism)

This is one of the strongest influences on young people. The fact that they can get enjoyment from a drug of their choice is important. Recreational drug users will give positive reasons for their decision to take drugs; for example, they might say 'it makes me feel good'.

Age

This is a factor which influences young people to experiment with drugs because of their natural curiosity and risk-taking behaviour. The age of a young person also dictates, to a certain extent, the type of drug they will use. For example, a person between the ages of 7 and 14 is more likely to be involved with using nicotine, alcohol, poppers and solvents. People in their late teens are more likely to experiment with heroin.

Gender (sex)

Early experimentation tends to be seen more in males than in females. However, these differences appear to level out or disappear as they get older.

Curiosity

This is an important influence on young people, especially in early stages of drug use (experimental or novice use). It must also be noted that some young people are more curious than others. Other influences may affect the level of curiosity, such as **peer groups**, media coverage of drug issues, how available the drug is, or the amount of money a young person has to spend on alternative activities.

Risk-taking (excitement)

It would appear that risk-taking is a normal part of growing up for young people. Using drugs is one way in which a young person takes risks. Teenagers often see themselves as indestructible when it comes to taking risks, thinking 'it will never happen to me' and 'I'm in control of the risks'.

Peer pressure

This is where a young person tries to gain the respect of their group of friends by adapting their set of norms (their set of values). This can involve taking or experimenting with drugs. The young person is often encouraged by the group of friends and therefore feels secure as part of the group.

Peer group

This is not to be confused with peer pressure. Here, the young person chooses a group of people (a peer group) to belong to that has the same or similar set of values and norms as he/she has. For example, if the person is misusing drugs, he/she will hang around with others who are misusing drugs.

Availability

This is an important factor affecting which drugs are misused. If a drug is easily available then it is also easily accessible. Many young people will try drugs (especially in the experimental stage) if they know the person they are dealing with or if it is seen to be the drug all their friends are using.

Family problems

This has often been mentioned as one of the reasons that young people take, or start taking, drugs. However, not all people growing up within a family that is having problems, or as part of a one-parent family, take or misuse drugs; there are many young people from stable, untroubled families who also misuse drugs.

Drug function

Some young people with experience of drugs take a specific drug for its effect. For example: some people may choose cannabis for its calming effect; amphetamines if they want to stay awake for long periods of time; ecstasy so they can dance for prolonged periods, etc.

Different drugs are taken for different effects.

Where you live

Drug use can be linked to certain socio-economic factors. For example, if there is poor housing, a lack of education, poor job prospects or high unemployment, low wages, a higher number of families with problems, etc., in an area, the risk of drug use may be increased. However, it is important to remember that drug use extends across all socio-economic levels.

To escape reality

Young people often say that they use drugs to escape from reality. They feel that drugs are a good, or sometimes the only, way to put their problems behind them. It helps them have a welcome break from the stresses of life. The problem here is that they then avoid dealing with the causes of their stresses. In reality they may get into more trouble by using drugs (e.g., with their family or the police for using or possessing drugs, or through physical harm to themselves from the effects of the drugs).

activities

Consider the 12 influences and pressures explained on the page opposite and above.

1. On your own, place these influences and pressures in order of importance. Make number one what you consider to be the most important and number twelve the least important.
2. Working in groups of either four or five, compare your ordered list of influences and pressures and agree on a group list from one to twelve.
3. State the reasons how and why your original list was different from the group response.

9. Licensing and retailing laws

Aims

At the end of this unit you should be able to:

- know the licensing and retailing laws
- understand the social issues relating to drug misuse.

The laws

In order to sell alcohol legally a licence must be obtained. The purpose of the licensing law is to control the level and pattern of alcohol consumption in order to protect social welfare and health in the community.

The Licensing (Northern Ireland) Order 1996 and the Registration of Clubs (Northern Ireland) Order 1996 came into effect on 20th February 1997.

The following changes to licensing and retailing laws were included in these new orders:

- The prohibition on 'mixed trading' was lifted, enabling shops to sell alcohol alongside other goods.
- Certificates for children were introduced allowing those under the age of 18, and accompanied by an adult, to be in licensed premises.
- Longer opening hours were granted for off-licences, including Sunday opening.
- Licensed premises were granted permission to sell alcohol between 2.30 p.m. and 7.00 p.m. on Sundays.
- Smaller pubs were granted permission to sell alcohol for additional hours on 20 occasions per year, without having to provide food or entertainment.
- Restaurants were given permission to have licensed bars.

activity

In Northern Ireland, the courts process all applications for licences to permit the sale of intoxicating liquor. There are a number of different opening hours depending on the type of establishment. Using the website www.drugsalcohol.info/alcohol find out the specific opening hours that are allowed under each of the following establishment's licences.

- Public house
- Restaurant
- Guest house
- Higher education institute
- Registered club
- Hotel
- Off-licence
- Conference centre
- Place of public entertainment

Alcohol, the law and young people

There are a number of provisions regarding the sale of alcohol to people under the age of 18, and its consumption.

It is an offence:

- for a licensee, or any of his/her employees, to permit anyone under the age of 18 to consume alcohol in licensed premises or in nearby premises under the licensee's control
- for anyone under the age of 18 to purchase alcohol
- for anyone under the age of 18 to consume alcohol in any place other than a private residence
- for any person under the age of 18 to pretend to be over 18 for the purpose of purchasing, obtaining or being allowed to consume alcohol
- for any person to purchase alcohol for someone under the age of 18

- for any young person to be in an off-licence unless accompanied by an adult (i.e., someone who is at least 18 years old)
- for a person under the age of 18 to be in any part of licensed premises which contain a bar, or which are wholly or exclusively used for the sale and consumption of alcohol, unless a children's certificate is in force.

In addition, under the Children's and Young Person's Act (Northern Ireland) 1968, it is an offence to give alcohol to any child under the age of 14 (whether or not in a private residence) unless for medical treatment.

As well as these licensing laws, there are other laws to penalise anti-social behaviour resulting from the consumption of alcohol. The two main types are public drunkenness, and drinking and driving.

Drunkenness

There is no 'drunk and disorderly' offence in Northern Ireland. The offence is called 'disorderly behaviour', and the person charged may or may not have consumed alcohol. The charge of 'simple drunk' is more often used as a protection for the drinker than the more serious offence of disruptive drunkenness that carries a more serious penalty.

Drinking in public places

Due to public anxiety over drunken behaviour in public places (e.g., town centres) local council by-laws have been introduced which make it an offence to consume alcohol in designated public places.

Drinking and driving

The law states clearly that it is an offence to drive with an alcohol level above:

- 80 milligrams of alcohol per 100 millilitres of blood
- 107 milligrams of alcohol per 100 millilitres of urine
- 35 micrograms of alcohol per 100 millilitres of breath.

This person is being breathalysed to see if they have too much alcohol in their breath.

Social issues regarding drugs

The following statements present topical social issues regarding the use of drugs:

Issue 1

Cannabis should be legalised.

Issue 2

Young people use drugs (including alcohol) for a variety of reasons, but the main reason is that they are bored.

Issue 3

Drinking and driving has continued to be a serious social problem.

activity

Work on your own or as a group to research these three statements above regarding drugs, young people and society. Compile your findings and prepare a class presentation. You can use books, CD-ROMs, the Internet, videos or your own experience or opinions.

For example, for issue 1, consider the way cannabis is taken, whether it is addictive, whether people die from taking it, the effects/risks of taking it, whether it has any medical use, etc. For issue 2, consider what alternative activities young people could take part in which do not carry the stigma or risks of drugs. For issue 3, consider the heavy penalties for being caught and the advertising campaigns warning of the consequences of drink-driving and whether attitudes are changing or not.

10. Personal development

Aims

At the end of this unit you should be able to:

- define what is meant by personal development
- identify what factors contribute to personal development.

What is personal development?

When we are born we are not a finished product. We have the potential to face life and all its challenges. Personal development is about realising our capacity to become whole, functioning adults with a high quality of life. It is about maximising our potential and finding the best processes to grow, change and develop to become a worthwhile human being.

In unit 2, you considered the World Health Organisation's (WHO) definition of health as: 'A complete state of physical, mental and social wellbeing and not simply the absence of disease or infirmity.' This supports the idea of personal development, which can be defined as: 'A lifelong process of learning, refining and making sense of ourselves as individuals, our relationships with others and the society in which we live.'

Personal development is a process within which we may learn to:

- examine the values that shape and form our attitudes and behaviours
- reflect on past experience and consider the choices for future action
- understand that all decisions have consequences, both good and bad
- develop **self-esteem** and confidence
- recognise our strengths and weaknesses and be able to make changes in our lives
- take control and responsibility for our own development
- develop respect for ourselves and others
- make and maintain safe and healthy relationships throughout our lifetime.

Contributing factors

There are six major areas that contribute to our personal development. These are identified in 'The Whole Person' diagram (opposite).

Physical development

(1) This is where we learn the importance of caring for our bodies (e.g., fitness, a balanced diet, exercise, sleep, etc.).

Academic/psychological development

This is where we discover how to enjoy the learning process so that we can become effective contributors to relationships and society.

Sexual development

This is when we become aware of our own **sexuality**, the changes that occur during adolescence and puberty, and develop our potential to connect with people and relate to them.

Moral development

(2) This is where we learn to develop our own attitudes and values which influence how we feel and react to situations. It enables us to know what is good or bad, healthy or unhealthy, or right or wrong in our lives.

Spiritual development

(3) This is brought about by the influence of religion or faith on our lives and behaviour. This development enables us to love and find truth, to trust and be honest with ourselves and others.

Social/emotional development

This is where we learn the ability to identify, understand, articulate and appropriately process our feelings, cope with stress and develop self-esteem.

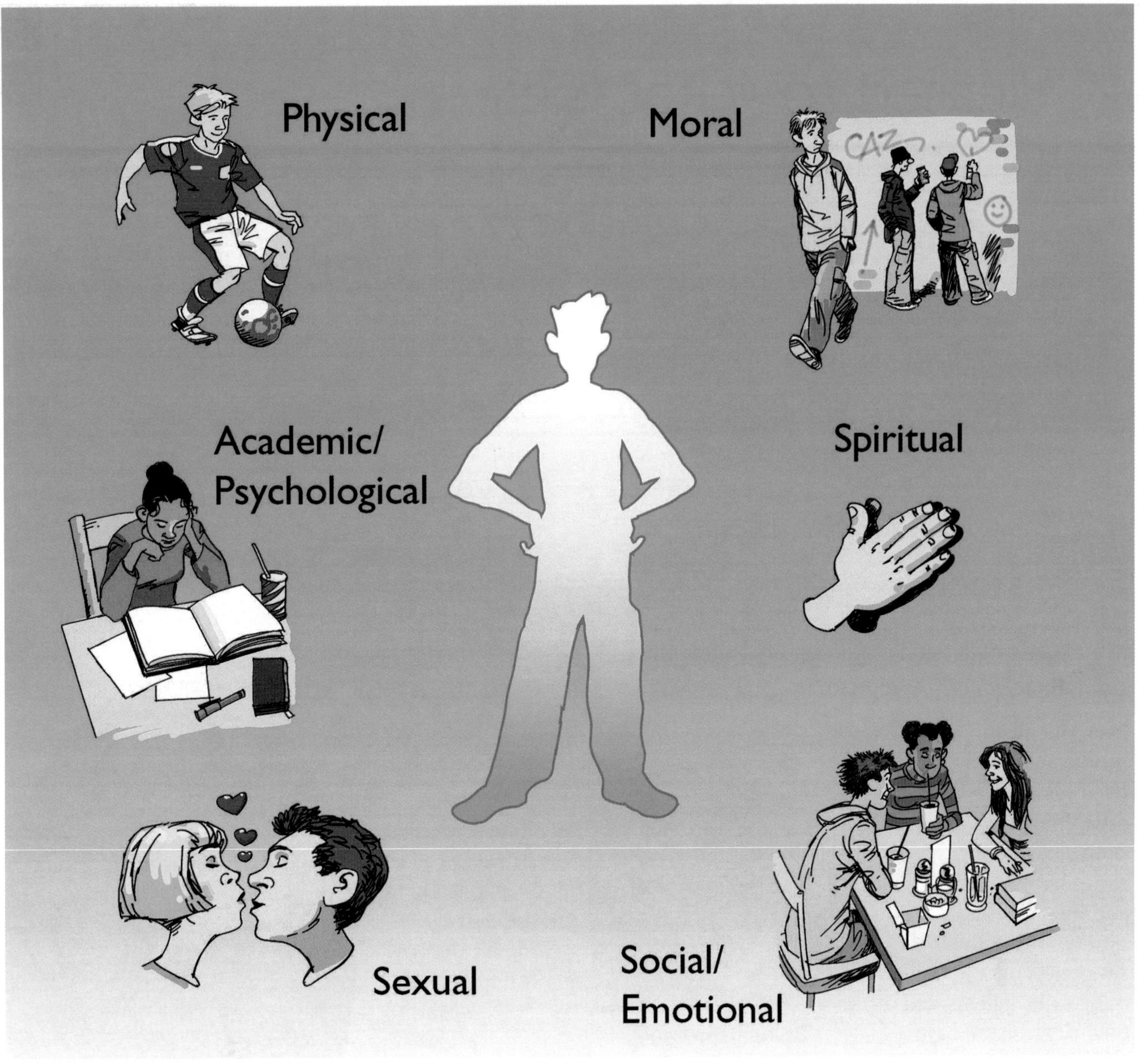

The Whole Person

activity

What affects personal development?

- Draw a circle and write down, inside it, all the factors that affect personal development *which are to do with the individual* (e.g., self-esteem, values, etc.).
- Draw a larger circle around the first circle and write down all the external factors that affect personal development (e.g., friends, school, media, etc.).
- Suggest how some of the external factors you have identified in the outer circle might connect with and influence the individual factors in the inner circle.
- Write your own definition for personal development based on what you have discovered.

11. 'Pleased to meet me!'

Aims

At the end of this unit you should be able to:

- appreciate your own uniqueness, importance and value
- understand what is meant by self-esteem, **self-confidence** and **self-respect** and learn how to go about increasing them
- identify your own strengths and weaknesses.

Self-esteem

Self-esteem means having a good opinion of yourself. It is based on understanding what your strengths are and valuing yourself as a person.

Everyone is unique! No two people are exactly the same. Even identical twins have different personalities and skills. Everyone has a unique combination of skills, talents and qualities that make him/her an individual. Awareness of, and belief in, these skills, talents and qualities leads to high self-esteem.

Being happy and confident leads to high self-esteem.

activity

- Make a list of the things you are 'good at', and a list of the things you are 'not so good at'.
- Discuss with a partner the things you've included that make you feel good and that you are most proud of.
- Choose one thing from your 'not so good at' list. Discuss with your partner something positive that you could do in order to get better at this.

Why is self-esteem important?

Self-esteem is important because it enables you to have the confidence to be yourself. With self-esteem you are able to say what you think and do what you think is right, rather than say and do things to impress others.

David's story

My friends all wanted to go up in a hot-air balloon. So when Ben's father fixed it for us they all got really excited. But I felt worried, because I'm really scared of heights, and I knew I couldn't face it.

Everyone crowded round me, teasing me and calling me all kinds of names. I felt dreadful about it.

Then I put my foot down. I said I wasn't going up, and I didn't care what they thought of me. End of story. Everyone calmed down then, and didn't tease me any more. But I went along on the morning of the flight and took some great photographs of the lift-off!

activities

1. Read David's story opposite and describe how you think David's self-esteem was affected by this experience.
2. Many young people find themselves in similar situations. It can be hard to do what is right, because of peer pressure. In groups:
   - Think of a difficult situation a young person your age may face.
   - Write it down on a piece of card.
   - Pass the card on to the next group.
   - Read the situation on the card you have been passed.
   - As a group, suggest a suitable response that you feel will result in maintaining the respect and esteem of the individual involved.
   - Present your suggestions in a class discussion.

Self-confidence

Confidence comes from believing in yourself and feeling happy. Self-esteem will give you the confidence to try new experiences, to achieve more and help develop a positive attitude that makes it easier to deal with setbacks.

Unrealistic expectations can damage self-confidence. We need to set ourselves achievable, but worthwhile, targets and believe that they can be met.

activity

Sometimes we all feel we just cannot do something. We do not feel at all confident!

- Write down a situation where someone might lack confidence (e.g., starting a new school).
- List some of the negative thoughts this person might have.
- In small groups, discuss what you have written and think of ways in which each negative thought could be turned into a positive thought.

Self-respect

Self-respect means having your own values and trying to live your life by them. Different people have different values; many can be shared by whole communities (e.g., that it is wrong to steal). Self-respect includes respecting the values of other people even if we do not agree with them!

activity

Study the following six statements. In pairs, talk about each one in turn, saying why you agree or disagree with it.

Make notes of your views and share them in a class discussion.

1. What other people think of you and your behaviour is more important than what you think about yourself.
2. It's not being 'big-headed' to feel proud of yourself and your achievements.
3. It's not what you look like that matters, it's what kind of person you are and how you feel about yourself.
4. If you're not confident about doing something, it's better to avoid doing it rather than risk making a fool of yourself.
5. People who keep putting you down only do so to try to make themselves feel better.
6. Imitating other people, by doing whatever is cool and trendy, is the best way to boost your confidence.

Is looking the same as your friends important to you?

12. Managing influences

Aims

At the end of this unit you should be able to:

- identify **peer influences** and know how they can have both a good and a bad effect on behaviour
- identify and evaluate the types of messages coming from the media and know whether they are good or bad
- understand the motives behind media advertising
- understand how the media influences behaviour.

Being 'part of the crowd'

For most young people, fitting in is extremely important. Have you ever noticed how some groups of people wear similar clothes, or listen to the same type of music? Imagine how you would feel to discover that you were wearing completely different clothes to the rest of your friends!

Group or 'peer' influence affects us all in some way. It is a natural part of human behaviour, but not all influences are in our best interest!

Why might this group of teenagers feel as if they fit in?

Peer influence

Most people change their behaviour in certain situations to help them feel comfortable. However, pressures from other people or groups sometimes make us behave in ways that we are not comfortable with. For example, at a party a young person may find himself/herself being pressured into doing something with their partner that they don't want to do, because of pressure from the partner or friends. The phrase: 'If you really loved me you would …' is a classic form of peer pressure used in relationships.

It can be very difficult to resist these pressures, but knowing what feels right or wrong and what behaviour feels comfortable can help.

activity

- Think of how you have recently been influenced by one of your friends.
- In small groups come up with as many different influences as you can.
- Now try to divide these into good influences and bad influences.
- Consider how you decide whether something is 'good' or 'bad'.
- Consider which influences are most difficult to resist and why.

Media messages

Communication is about sending and receiving messages. This is done through the media (e.g., newspapers, magazines, television, the Internet, text messages on mobile phones, films, radio, etc.).

We are all influenced by what we see, hear or read! For example, think about the last time you bought new clothes, shoes, a CD or got your hair cut. What or who influenced your decision? Chances are that you saw someone famous in a magazine or on television who had something similar and you thought it looked or sounded cool!

Do media messages influence our lives?

activity

Copy the table below and add as many things as you can think of that could be influenced by the media. Then, using stars, indicate the extent to which you think each type of media influences your choices.

*** = a lot   ** = some   * = a little   no stars = not at all

	Television	Magazines	Newspapers	Films/ Videos	Adverts	Radio	Internet
Clothes							
Shoes							
Sportswear							

Types of media messages

- The messages portrayed by the newspapers, magazines and television are very powerful. The information we receive will be influenced by the government, newspaper owners and advertising companies. Some of this information may provide positive messages (e.g., the importance of regular exercise or a healthy diet). Other information can result in negative messages: features on glamour models and advertisements for top of the range sports cars create desires for things that many of us cannot achieve.
- Television adverts show young people drinking unmeasured spirits, dancing in skimpy clothes and having a great time. No one is ever sick or getting unwanted attention! This is a misleading portrayal of life. People who try to recreate these adverts may be disappointed by real life!
- When watching television dramas and soap operas, the acting is often quite convincing and the setting so realistic that you can easily forget that you are watching a fictional story. Again, these create misleading portrayals of life. People who try to live up to what they see on television may be disappointed by real life!

Most young people aged between 5 and 14 years watch over 20 hours of television each week!

activity

Write a review of a soap opera that you watch and include the following points:

- What dramatic events have been included to capture your attention?
- How realistic are these events?
- What messages are being portrayed?
- Are they good/healthy messages or bad/unhealthy messages?
- Who would be most influenced by these messages?

You could do a similar type of activity using some teenage magazines as research material.

Media advertising

The role of the advertising company is to influence our behaviour so that our actions make them money. This could be to buy a particular product or to go to a particular venue. There have been many complaints about advertisements and how they are targeted at young people, negatively influencing their behaviour (e.g., the increasing number of sexual images and innuendos used in many advertising campaigns).

activity

Use a selection of magazines and cut out all the advertisements. Consider the following:

- What is being advertised?
- Who is being targeted by the advert?
- How is the product being promoted?
- How might it influence the reader's behaviour?

13. Personal messages

Aims

At the end of this unit you should be able to:

- understand the nature of body language and the messages it portrays
- appreciate the influence of make-up and fashion on non-verbal communication
- understand how the way you speak or move implies hidden personal messages.

Body language

Our **body language** often reveals more than what we say. You will probably have heard the expressions: 'It was written all over his face' and 'I can see it in your eyes'. These expressions refer to the non-verbal messages portrayed by body language.

Body language is a natural part of human behaviour which is particularly important before we learn how to speak. As we get older it reveals a lot about how we are feeling within ourselves and towards others. For example, crossed arms and raised eyes can indicate defensive behaviour, and smiles and eye contact can indicate open confidence in the other person.

By learning to have some control over body language, people can avoid giving others the wrong impression about their feelings and intentions.

activity

'Can you speak the lingo?'

Look at the first three pictures (a to c).

- What messages are their bodies telling you about how they are feeling?
- Which person would you most like to have a cup of coffee with? Give reasons for your choice.

Now look at the next three pictures (d to f). Which person would you say was the most honest? Give reasons for your choice.

a

b

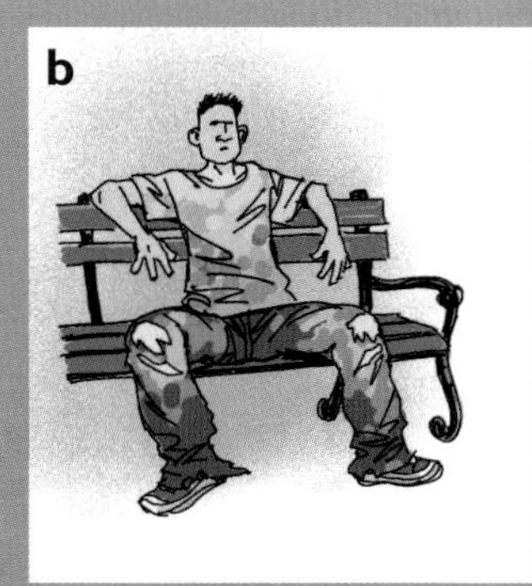

c

d

e

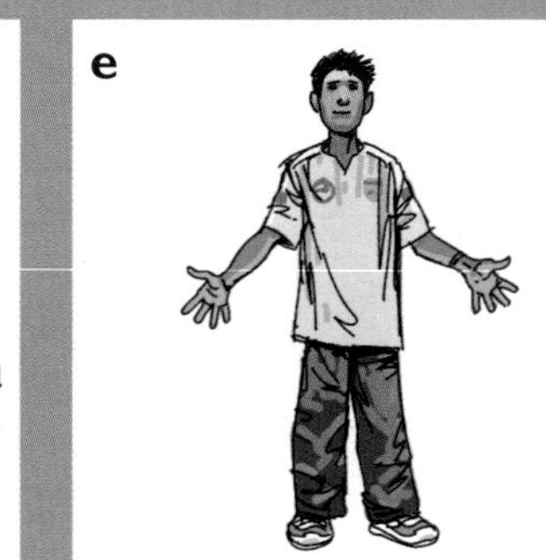

f

Clothes and make-up

There can be no doubt that clothes affect the way we feel and act. Think how different you feel wearing school uniform compared with old jeans and a sweatshirt!

Clothes send messages about what type of people we are. The danger comes when these messages are not what we intended.

Girls dressed in short skirts and revealing tops may unknowingly be sending out messages that suggest to boys they are interested in sex. Boys dressed in leather jackets and ripped jeans may be sending out messages that suggest they are tough and looking for a fight!

Make-up may make us look more grown up but applied in a certain way can give totally the wrong message.

Do you mean what you say?

There are often hidden messages in what people say and how they say things. For example, by using 'bad language' we are sending messages about ourselves to those who hear it. Many young people use bad language to make themselves seem more grown up or tough, but is that the result? If you were being interviewed for a part-time job, would you use bad language during the interview? If not, why not?

Even the tone of our voice presents a hidden message. The bottom line is that we communicate much more than the words we speak. If we are aware of this, we can try to make sure the messages are what we intend them to be, and not likely to attract unwanted attention.

activities

1. What impressions do you get when you look at the two pictures on the right? State why the pictures make you think this way.
2. Present as many different messages as you can in a role play using the phrases: 'You're looking well today' and 'I love your hair'. Be aware of how you can completely change the message by the tone of your voice.

14. Relationships

Aims

At the end of this unit you should be able to:

- identify different types of relationships
- understand the factors necessary to develop a relationship
- determine whether different factors are needed to maintain a relationship.

Types of relationships

Throughout our lives we become involved in a variety of relationships. These will be with family, friends, work colleagues, boy/girlfriends, love/sexual relationships or marriage.

Families

There can be no doubt that families have changed dramatically over the last century. Around 42% of marriages now end in divorce and many couples do not get married at all. There are more one-parent families or 'blended' families where parents remarry and have children from the different relationships living together.

All of these factors will have an effect on the types of relationships that occur in families; they can make understanding and coping with family relationships quite a challenge!

The 'traditional' family.

One-parent families are very common now.

Friends

People of all ages tend to have a wide circle of friends outside their family. Very often, people make friends with those who share the same interests, who have been placed in the same class in school, or who live nearby.

There are different levels of friendship:

The acquaintance someone you know a little about, but don't spend much time with.

The companion someone in your circle of friends with whom you spend quite a lot of time. You know them well and can share things easily with them.

The close friend someone you can share things with on a more intimate level. There is a high level of trust and confidence between you.

activities

1. Write down five things you would look for in a friend. List them in order of importance.
2. Copy the following diagram and copy and complete the sentences below about your friends and family. Now add the names to your diagram.
   - The person who is closest to me is … because …
   - The next closest to me is … because …
   - The person who is quite far away from me is … because …
   - I have a more distant relationship with … because …
   - The person who is most remote is … because …

Boy/Girlfriends

During the teenage years some boys and girls pair off into more serious relationships and have a steady boy/girlfriend. They are still friends, but they also feel a sexual interest in each other. What makes someone attractive to the opposite sex? Some say good looks, but others argue that personality is important.

Two things are particularly important in any boy/girlfriend relationship:

- Respect for the other person and a wish for that person's happiness and well-being.
- Responsibility for understanding that all that takes place between them will not be regretted in the future.

activity

- What qualities do you look for in a girl/boyfriend? List them in order of importance.
- Working in groups, compare your lists.
- Does everyone look for the same things in their relationships?
- What are the differences between your list and the other lists in your group? Think of reasons why this might be.

Love and sexual relationships

The statement that boys are interested in sex whereas girls are interested in love often creates lively discussion with girls complaining about the sexual excesses of boys.

It is a biological fact that boys are more easily sexually aroused than girls. A common generalisation or **stereotype** is that boys can separate sex more easily from emotion. However, boys do look for a range of qualities in girls (e.g., physical attractiveness, intelligence, friendliness, maturity and personality).

Girls look for similar qualities in boys, but, particularly during adolescence, they have a greater need for emotional involvement before they are happy to engage in sexual activity. They are more likely than boys to want a steady relationship and the security that accompanies it. It is a common stereotype that girls dream of the ideal man, perfect wedding and beautiful home, viewing the world through rose-tinted glasses. This stereotypical view of the sexes decreases on progression into adulthood where there is less of a gender gap in terms of attitudes towards sex.

Love, marriage and sex

Often the word 'love' is used to mean no more than 'like' (e.g., 'I love fish and chips'). It can also refer to the love shown towards a friend, the affection for parents and family, a crush on a pop star or the physical excitement in a sexual relationship.

There is so much more involved in love than sexual desire and satisfaction. Sex as a physical urge separated from love can become a mechanical act; although, on the other hand, the physical closeness of sex can sometimes be wrongly mistaken for a deeper relationship!

In a loving relationship (heterosexual or homosexual) where there is sexual attraction, sexual activity does not necessarily play an immediate part. Many people believe that sexual intercourse should only take place after marriage or in a permanent loving relationship.

Whatever your views are, it should be realised that the deepest kind of love, 'true' love, involves caring, sacrifice, giving without expecting anything in return, putting the other person's feelings first and accepting the other person for what they are. Love at this depth is not selfish and there can be no manipulation.

'For better or for worse' ... true love.

15. The 3 'r's of relationships

Aims

At the end of this unit you should be able to:

- understand the rights of individuals, the roles that they take on and the responsibilities that go with relationships
- appreciate the implications of sharing, commitment and respect within relationships
- examine sexual stereotyping and how it affects our lives.

Rights and responsibilities

With the increasing awareness of the **European Convention on Human Rights** (**ECHR**) and its application to our lives in general, people are now more aware that they have rights in society. But with rights come responsibility; the two cannot be separated, particularly in relationships.

Within a relationship both parties have their own rights, such as:

The right to be treated with respect.
The right to express my feelings.
The right to say yes or no.
The right to feel safe.
The right to my own opinion.

With these rights come responsibilities such as:

To treat others the way I would like to be treated.
Not to make others suffer just to get what I want.
To be aware of, and respect the rights of, others.
To accept the consequences of my actions.

activity

In groups, discuss and draw up a list of rights for an individual in a relationship.

Consider what responsibilities would come with these rights. For example:

- 'I have the right to make mistakes.'
- 'I must accept responsibility for the consequences of my mistakes.'

Roles in a relationship

The roles of individuals in their relationships have changed dramatically since the Second World War. With the push towards equality, the traditional roles of men and women have become blurred and this can cause confusion and misunderstanding within a relationship. For example, men used to be seen as the dominant partner who took responsibility for making the decisions. They were the provider and the protector. Women, on the other hand, were expected to abide by the decisions of their partner. They cooked, cleaned and looked after the children. 'A woman's place *was* in the home.'

Traditional male image

A woman's place ...

Today, this stereotypical image has changed, with the roles less clearly defined. However, it could not be said that the traditional male and female roles have disappeared altogether!

activities

1. Discuss how the roles of men and women in relationships have changed today. Which traditional roles have disappeared and which ones still remain?
2. Make a list of the roles taken on by young people in a relationship. For example: Who makes the decisions? Who pays for the cinema? Who washes the dishes? Would these roles change if they were married or living together?

Whatever role is taken on by an individual it is important to realise that it brings with it responsibilities and that as we get older these responsibilities will change, particularly if the nature of the relationship changes too.

Within any relationship, certain factors are very important and have a major effect.

Sharing not just of money or material possessions, but thoughts, feelings, needs and desires, all necessary in a healthy relationship.

Commitment to the relationship, to stay with that person even when things get tough. To be prepared to make sacrifices for the good of the relationship and to stand by and support the other person when he/she needs it.

Respect for yourself, so that you do not do things that make you feel uncomfortable, and for your partner, so that you consider their feelings, needs and faults and can accept them for who they are and not what you may want them to be.

Stereotyping

Stereotyping involves judging people on the basis of a group to which they belong, often in an insulting way. This may be based on gender, race, age, religion, hobby, occupation, disability, lifestyle, sexual orientation, habitat, employment status and social class. We tend to develop negative and positive attitudes towards people based on such judgements. Stereotyping can affect people's opportunities in life.

Even with the advent of equality in our society, there is still very clear sexual stereotyping between men and women. A common stereotype is that women still have responsibility for bringing up children, doing the shopping and organising family meals. Men are still stereotyped as being the major wage-earner, having to do all the DIY tasks and make the major decisions. These stereotypes are still true in some cases. Things are changing, but have they changed as much as we think?

Statistical evidence indicates that inequalities still exist. For example:

- the number of women in parliament is only 118 out of 659
- the average earnings of women are 82% of those of men. However, this gap did narrow by 1% between April 2002 and April 2003, which shows how the situation is getting better.

activities

1. Consider your favourite television soap.
   - What stereotypes are enforced about men and women?
   - Are these stereotypes accurate when applied to real life?
   - What damage can be done by creating such stereotypes?
2. Think of three groups who are often stereotyped. For each group write down what the stereotype is and comment on why you think it is unfair.

A businessman greeting his female secretary. Do you think men and women are still stereotyped in the workplace?

16. Sexual identity and orientation

Aims

At the end of this unit you should be able to:

- understand what is meant by sexuality
- be aware of different sexual identities and orientations
- appreciate and respect the variety of views, including your own, surrounding **homosexuality**
- have a clear understanding of the laws surrounding sex.

What is sexuality?

Sexuality concerns people's feelings about being male or female and how they deal with these feelings. This is easier to understand when divided into three parts:

Sexual orientation a person's primary sexual attraction to the same, opposite or both sexes.

Sexual identity how people see themselves and present themselves to others.

Loving relationships exist between different and the same sexes.

Sexual behaviour what a person does, sexually. This does not always match a person's sexual identity or sexual orientation.

During adolescence, some people experience strong emotional attachments and feelings towards people of their own sex. Many move on to form **heterosexual** relationships; some remain permanently homosexual or **bisexual**.

activities

1. Match the following words with the statements below: heterosexual, homosexual, **lesbian**, bisexual, **transsexual**, **gay man**, **celibate**.
   - A person who feels very strongly that they were born with the body of one sex and the mind of the other sex.
   - A person who is attracted to and has sexual relationships with both men and women.
   - A man who is attracted to and has sexual relationships with men.
   - A person who is attracted to and has sexual relationships with people of the opposite sex.
   - A person who is attracted to and has sexual relationships with people of the same sex.
   - A woman who is attracted to and has sexual relationships with women.
   - A person who does not have sexual activity with other people.
2. In small groups come up with a definition of your own understanding of the word sexuality.
3. What factors might influence or inhibit people's sexuality (e.g., friends' opinions, parents' expectations, etc.)?

Sex and the law

The law in Northern Ireland

Heterosexual sex

- The age of consent is 17 in Northern Ireland.
- The maximum penalty for a man who has sex with an underaged girl is two years' imprisonment if the girl is aged between 14 and 17 years. The maximum penalty is life if the girl is under 14 years old.
- Only the male is liable for prosecution; there is no defence that the man believed the girl to be 17 or over.
- The law does not refer to unlawful sexual intercourse between a woman and a male who is under 16 years of age. However, a woman could be charged with indecent assault.

Homosexual sex

Sex between men there are specific legal requirements requiring privacy which apply only to male homosexual sex. In 'private' means that no more than two people should be present and that sex should not take place in a public toilet.

- The age of sexual consent is 17 in Northern Ireland.
- A male person under 17 is not committing an offence himself if he engages in certain homosexual acts with another male over 17. Both are committing an offence if they are both under the age of 17.

Sex between women sex between women is legal provided that both of the women concerned consent and are 16 or over.

activities

1. In small groups, discuss the laws around sex and consider the following issues:
   - Do you agree or disagree with the laws?
   - Are the laws fair? If not, why not?
   - Should the laws be different for men and women?
2. In small groups, write the following headings on six large pieces of paper: heterosexual man, heterosexual woman, gay man, lesbian, celibate man, celibate woman.
   - Write down all the words and phrases you can think of relating to the heading on each page.
   - Decide which of the words or phrases are positive (+ve) and which are negative (-ve). Record your decisions on each page.
   - Now discuss the words you have come up with using these discussion points to help you.

Discussion points

- Discuss why some words or phrases created for the headings are more positive or negative than others, and why.
- Are some of the words particularly aggressive? If so, what does this tell us about the way people who are different from the majority are treated by other people?
- Why are some people so negative about other people who may be different from themselves? What are they scared of?
- What can be done to promote a more positive image of people who are different from the majority?

17. Sexual harassment and abuse

Aims

At the end of this unit you should be able to:

- understand the meaning of **sexual harassment** and abuse
- be aware of the human rights issues associated with both harassment and abuse
- have an awareness of relevant support agencies
- know the difference between intercourse and **rape**, its implications and the law surrounding rape.

What is sexual harassment?

Sexual harassment is unwelcome sexual behaviour. It is not about fun or friendship: it is about the abuse of power. Since there is no single definition, the test is how the recipient feels about the behaviour. The vast majority of complaints of sexual harassment have been by women against men – it has been estimated that 50% of women in employment are affected by such harassment.

Everyone has a legal right not to be sexually harassed. The Sex Discrimination Act 1975 protects people against sexual harassment in the workplace. This means that if someone is sexually harassed at work they could make a complaint and take their case to an employment tribunal.

Sexual harassment can take many forms:

1. Verbal

- comments about appearance, body or clothes
- indecent remarks
- questions or comments about your sex life

'Relax, it's just a bit of fun!'

- sexual demands made by someone of the opposite sex, or by someone of your own sex
- promises or threats concerning a person's employment conditions in return for sexual favours.

2. Non-verbal

- looking or staring at a person's body
- display of sexually explicit material, such as calendars, pin-ups or magazines.

3. Physical

- physically touching, pinching, caressing, kissing or hugging
- **sexual assault**
- rape.

Sexual assault and some forms of harassment can actually be criminal offences, in which case you can report them to the police.

What is abuse?

Abuse involves treating others in a way that is physically or mentally harmful to them.

Types of abuse include:

Neglect when a parent fails to meet a child's basic needs for food, warmth, clothing and medical attention. It can also mean leaving a child to fend for itself when it is very young.

Physical deliberate injury of a child/adult (e.g., being hit, shaken, burned, kicked, etc.).

Verbal shouting, using foul language.

Emotional when a parent continually fails to show love and affection to a child or to constantly use sarcasm, threaten, criticise, shout at or taunt a child. This also applies to adults.

Sexual when an adult, or sometimes an older child, uses a child for sexual gratification (e.g., being forced to carry out sexual touching or intercourse).

Victims of abuse often feel embarrassed, guilty or ashamed, and fear the consequences of revealing what is going on. They may either think they are the only ones suffering in this way, or that what is happening to them is normal.

... I have to promise not to tell anyone. He says if I do he will say it's my fault, that I want to do it because I'm bad! When I was little I used to think everyone's uncle did this, but now I know it's only mine. I'm so miserable, I hate it every time he comes to the house, but what can I do? If I try to avoid him Mum says I'm being rude. I can't tell her in case she doesn't believe me. I can't take much more of this.

... she keeps on about how stupid I am and that I'm rubbish at everything. She says it to everyone and laughs about it, making me say I'm stupid over and over again! She's full of praise for the others, tells everybody how clever they are. If I don't say what she wants I get sent to my room. She even gave my birthday present from Gran away because I was 'being difficult'. I know I am stupid, I must be, but how can I make her stop?

... he's always sorry afterwards, but when things get to him he just seems to snap. Mum gets the worst of it but he belts me too at times and I have to stay off school until the bruises fade. I'm scared he will start on my younger brother and sister. If I tell anyone Mum says it will break up the family. I don't know what to do.

activity

Read the accounts above, then answer the following questions. Write down what feelings and type of abuse each person might be experiencing.

1. Why might people who are being abused be reluctant to take action to stop the abuse?
2. What actions might someone take if they were being abused?

Human Rights Act 1998

Under Article 3 of the Human Rights Act, inhuman and degrading treatment is prohibited. The Human Rights Act also has some bearing on certain harassment matters, including sexual orientation, as, under Article 9, it provides the right to respect for private and family life.

Rape

Rape is 'unlawful sexual intercourse with a woman who at the time of intercourse, does not consent to it', where the rapist knows that she does not consent ... or is reckless as to whether she does or does not consent.

The law and rape

The Sexual Offences Act 2003 is said to offer a clear, coherent and effective set of laws that will increase protection of the victim, enable the appropriate punishment of abusers and ensure the law is fair and non-discriminatory. In other words, there will be no bias towards gender (e.g., making the assumption that the abuser must be male or that rape could not have happened because the couple were married).

It aims to offer stronger punishment for sexual violence.

activity

When someone is raped, it is not their fault. However, there are things you can do to reduce your chances of being raped or sexually assaulted.

- Make a list of things you could do to help protect yourself from sexual attack.
- Design a leaflet to help people of your age avoid situations where they may be at risk of sexual attack.
- Find out what support agencies are available to someone who has suffered abuse.

18. STIs and HIV

Aims

At the end of this unit you should be able to:

- define **STIs** and **HIV**
- identify the most common STIs and know their symptoms, health risks and treatment
- know how STIs are transmitted and how to prevent transmission.

What are STIs?

Sexually Transmitted Infections (STIs) are infections that are passed from one person to another through sexual contact. They affect the genital area as well as the bladder and so are sometimes called genito-urinary infections.

How do you get infected?

An STI is caught through having close sexual contact, including sexual intercourse, with an infected partner. They are very common and anyone who has sex can get infected. The more partners you have, the more you put yourself at risk.

'What's wrong? It's not as if you're going to catch anything!'

What is HIV?

HIV (Human Immunodeficiency Virus) is a virus which damages the body's immune system. When someone has **AIDS** (Acquired Immune Deficiency Syndrome) it means that they are HIV positive and have gone on to develop a series of serious illnesses.

How do you get infected?

HIV is only passed on through bodily fluids and blood, such as through sex without a condom with someone who has HIV, injecting drugs and from a mother to her unborn child. The only way to tell if someone has HIV is by having a blood test. To date, there is still no cure for HIV and AIDS.

activity

Answer the questions below using the information from the table opposite.

1. How many of these STIs are viral infections?
2. Which STIs are bacterial infections?
3. Which STIs could also be passed on by non-sexual contact?
4. Which STIs can be treated with antibiotics?
5. Which STIs cannot be cured?
6. Which STIs cause itching?
7. Which STIs cause pain when passing urine?
8. Which STIs can be treated with shampoos or lotions?
9. Which STIs can still be passed on even if a condom is used?

How to help prevent STIs

- Do not have sex.
- Only have sex with one uninfected partner for life who has only ever had sex with you.
- Using a condom makes sex safer, not safe.
- Reduce the number of sexual partners you have.
- Avoid high-risk sexual activities.
- Do not share needles.

The red ribbon is the international symbol for AIDS awareness.

Some of the most common STIs

STI	Caused by	Symptoms	Health risk	Treatment
Chlamydia	Bacteria passed on during sexual intercourse.	Most people don't have any symptoms. Can be discharge from the vagina/penis and pain when passing urine.	If untreated it can lead to Pelvic Inflammatory Disease (PID) which can lead to infertility in both men and women.	Antibiotics.
Genital warts	Virus passed on during sexual contact.	Can take 1–3 months for symptoms to appear and many people do not get any symptoms. They are small fleshy lumps like the warts that can be found on the hands. Can cause itching. Can appear in hard-to-see places like inside the vagina or on the cervix.	Warts are abnormal cellular growths and can be linked with genital cancers such as cervical cancer.	Small warts will clear up by themselves after 6 months. Larger clusters may need to be surgically removed. Freezing, laser or 'paint on' treatments are all options, but only after medical advice.
Genital herpes	Virus (Herpes Simplex Virus) passed on through skin contact with an infected person during sexual activity.	Symptoms may include: • stinging in the genital area • flu-like symptoms • pain in the legs or thighs • blisters which leave small, red, painful ulcers in the genital area • pain when passing urine.	Babies in the womb can be infected.	There is no cure. Attacks can be made less severe or less frequent by taking antiviral medication.
Gonorrhoea	Bacteria passed on during sexual intercourse.	Many people show no symptoms. Similar to chlamydia.	Can cause PID and infertility in both men and women.	Antibiotics.
Hepatitis Band C	Virus that causes your liver to swell. Passed on by sexual intercourse without a condom or sharing needles.	25% of patients may have no symptoms. The rest may develop nausea, jaundice, dark urine and grey-coloured stools, diarrhoea, weight loss and itchy skin. Flu-like symptoms may develop.	The virus can cause chronic infection which may result in cirrhosis or cancer of the liver.	There is no known cure. In some cases the body fights off the disease and the symptoms go away.
Syphilis	Bacteria passed on during sexual activities.	50% of people will be symptomless. Infectious sores appear 10 days to 3 months after contact, on the lips/ mouth and around the genital area and are painless. If untreated the next stage develops between 6 weeks and 6 months later. Symptoms may include headache, fatigue, low-grade fever, skin rash and enlarged lymph nodes.	Syphilis lesions increase the danger of becoming infected with HIV by 9 times. The virus can destroy the inner tissues and organs.	It is treated with a two-week course of penicillin injections or tablets.
Tricho-moniasis	Protozoan, a tiny parasite that can infect the urethra (urine passage) and vagina.	Up to 80% of men and 50% of women have no symptoms. Women may discover a yellow or white discharge from the vagina which can smell and also cause itching or skin irritation. Men may have a discharge or stingingness when passing urine.	No serious health risks.	Treated easily with antibiotics.

19. Contraception

Aims

At the end of this unit you should be able to:

- explore and evaluate issues concerning **abstinence** and sex outside marriage
- identify a range of **contraceptives** in terms of how they work and how they are used, their effectiveness and whether they prevent STIs
- understand the consequences of teenage pregnancy for both boys and girls, including emotional, social, financial, academic and moral.

Abstinence

The most effective way to prevent pregnancy (and catching an STI) is not to have sex. This is called abstinence. If two people do not have sex, the sperm cannot meet and fertilise the egg. This is, therefore, the only form of birth control which is 100% effective.

Many young people find that pressures from the media and friends push them into thinking that everyone is 'doing it' and so should they. In fact, this is not the case. A large proportion of young people are not having sex. Remember, once your virginity is lost, you cannot get it back. Many young people regret their first sexual experience and this can lead to low self-esteem. It is important that you make the right decision for you and not to please someone else.

Sex before marriage

Some people believe that sex before marriage is wrong. This can be because of religious views, where sex is promoted as a good thing but only within the context of marriage. There are advantages of waiting until you are married before having sex:

- you are less likely to be hurt or let down by bad or disappointing experiences of a sexual nature
- you will not be comparing your marital partner to any previous partners; nor will you be wondering (if your chosen partner is also a virgin) whether you live up to his/her previous experiences
- you are much less likely to catch an STI if both of you are virgins at marriage.

However, there are also a number of people for whom waiting until they are married to have sex is not a decision they want to make. They may choose not to get married, or want to explore the experience of sex without having to make a permanent commitment to someone.

Whatever decision you make, it must be right for you and considering the issues now may make it easier to make the choice later.

activity

Think of some of the consequences of having sex before marriage, both good and bad. Then, in the form of a table, write out three reasons for and against sex before marriage. Compare your answers in small groups and compile a top five in both categories.

The main types of contraception

Contraceptive	How it works	How effective it is	How it is used	Advantages	Disadvantages	Protects against STI?
Combined pill	Stops ovaries from releasing an egg (ovulation).	Over 99% effective if taken according to instructions.	1 pill taken every day for 21 days. 7 pill-free days.	Reduces bleeding, period pain and pre-menstrual tension (PMT). Protects against cancer of the ovary and womb.	Can cause temporary side-effects (e.g., headaches and nausea). More serious side-effects can be blood clots, breast and cervical cancers.	No.
Mini pill	Changes the mucus of the cervix and the lining of the uterus so egg cannot implant.	Over 99% effective if taken according to instructions.	1 pill taken every day.	It can be taken when breastfeeding. Good for women over 35 who smoke or are at risk of heart disease or strokes.	Periods may be irregular with bleeding in between cycles.	No.
Condom	Prevents sperm from meeting the egg.	98% effective if used according to instructions.	Thin rubber sheath is rolled over the erect penis.	Sold widely. Male takes responsibility for contraception.	Can slip off or split if not used properly. Man must withdraw straight after ejaculation and remove the condom.	Yes.
Female condom	Prevents sperm from meeting the egg.	95% effective if used according to instructions.	Thin plastic sheaths with rings at either end. Inserted into the vagina before intercourse.	Can be put in any time before sex. No prescription. Does not involve taking **hormones**.	Difficult to insert properly into the vagina. Penis can miss the condom and enter the vagina down the side.	Yes.
Diaphragm or cap with spermicide	Stops sperm getting through the cervix. Spermicide kills the sperm.	92–96% effective if used according to instructions.	Spermicidal gel is applied to the cap which is then pushed into place over the cervix inside the vagina by the woman.	Can be put in any time before sex. Does not involve taking hormones.	Increased risk of urinary infections. Need to be measured by the doctor so that the diaphragm fits properly. Need to reapply spermicide if having intercourse more than once.	No.
Implants under the skin	Thickens mucus in the cervix and thins the lining of the uterus so egg cannot implant.	Over 99% effective.	Small plastic tubes containing the hormone are placed under the skin of the upper arm.	Can last for up to 5 years before being removed.	Irregular periods with some bleeding in between cycles Other side effects can be acne and breast tenderness.	No.
IUS (intrauterine system)	Thickens mucus in the cervix and thins the lining of the uterus so egg cannot implant.	Over 99% effective.	A small plastic device containing the hormone progesterone is inserted into the uterus by a trained doctor or nurse.	Works for at least 3 years. Periods lighter and shorter.	Light bleeding between periods for first 3 months. May get temporary side-effects such as acne, headaches or breast tenderness.	No.
IUD (intra-uterine device or 'coil')	Blocks sperm moving up the uterus and prevents implantation.	98–99% effective.	A small plastic device is inserted into the uterus by a trained doctor or nurse.	Long-term, highly effective and reversible contraceptive.	Periods can be heavier or longer and more painful. Risk of infection of fallopian tubes.	No.

Emergency contraception

There are two types of emergency contraception:

1. Emergency pills must be taken within three days (72 hours) if you have had unprotected sex; the earlier you take them, the more likely they are to be successful.
2. An IUD can be fitted within five days of having unprotected sex.

activity

Use the information from the table on page 43 to answer these questions:

1. Name the contraceptives that contain hormones.
2. Which contraceptives give protection from STIs?
3. Which contraceptives do you not have to remember to take each day or when you are going to have sex?
4. What is the difference between the IUD and the IUS?
5. What group of women should not take the combined pill?
6. Which contraceptive requires the person to be measured by the doctor?

Views about contraception

- **'If young people can easily get contraceptives they are more likely to have sex.'**
- **'Contraceptives should be made available to young people in schools.'**
- **'Most young people are too shy to discuss contraception with their partner.'**
- **'Life begins at conception; therefore any contraceptive that works by preventing implantation of the embryo is morally wrong.'**

Teenage pregnancy

Very few sexually active young people believe that becoming pregnant will ever happen to them. However, each year there are approximately 1,700 births to teenage mothers and the numbers have been rising since 1995. The majority of teenage mothers are aged 18–19 but, between 1989 and 1998, there was an average of eight births per year to mothers under the age of 15, with a steep rise in births to mothers between the ages of 15 and 17.

Age	Total births (1989–1998)	Average no. of births per year
<14	12	1.2
14	65	6.5
15	343	34.3
16	1298	129.8
17	3222	322.2
18	5303	530.3
19	6709	670.9

Total and average number of births 1989–1998 by age.

While some teenage parents and their children live happy and fulfilled lives, far too many do not. Teenage parents can find themselves isolated from school, friends and society in general. They can suffer from poor physical and mental health and, because of the cost of raising a child, they may face poverty.

With a break in education or training, teenage parents (particularly the mothers) lose the opportunity to realise their full potential in the workplace and often end up with low-paid, low-status jobs or unemployed and dependant on state benefits.

Teenage fathers, faced with becoming financially responsible for their child, may not be able to continue with their educational plans and may have to get a job. They may also experience emotional problems at being separated from their child if access is not permitted.

Becoming a teenage parent can seriously affect your education and job opportunities.

activity

Design two leaflets, one for girls and one for boys, informing them of the consequences associated with becoming a teenage parent.

20. Where to find help

Aims

At the end of this unit you should be able to:

- highlight the range of support agencies available and know what services they provide
- know how to go about accessing services.

There are a variety of ways to obtain advice, help and support concerning sexual and other health matters. A good place to start is often a parent or carer, or maybe a teacher you have a good relationship with and feel you can trust. For medical advice, a selection of people are available to you:

- your GP, who will treat anything you discuss with them in the strictest of confidence
- Family Planning Clinic staff
- your school nurse
- staff at a genito-urinary clinic who treat STIs.

Of course, there are always friends who will be there to give moral support but they are often not the best people to go to for medical advice!

Below is a selection of agencies that are a good source of information and support for a variety of issues.

Other useful websites

www.loveforlife.org.uk
www.likeitis.org.uk
www.mindbodysoul.gov.uk
www.coolsexinfo.org.uk
www.hebs.com/thinkaboutit
www.playingsafely.co.uk
www.bbc.co.uk/health/sex
www.ruthinking.co.uk
www.teenshealth.org
www.nspcc.co.uk

Address	Service offered
Health Promotion Agency for Northern Ireland www.healthpromotionagency.org.uk	Provides leadership and strategic direction to all those involved in promoting health in Northern Ireland.
Childline Northern Ireland www.childline.org.uk	Free national helpline for children and young people in trouble or danger. Open 24 hours a day, every day of the week.
Family Planning Association Northern Ireland www.fpa.org.uk	Provides a confidential helpline service, a wide range of sexual health publications, training and consultancy for professionals and community workers, community projects and an unplanned pregnancy counselling service.
Nexus Institute www.nexusinstitute.org	Working to respond to the needs of adults who have experienced sexual abuse and to increase awareness of sexual abuse and its consequences.

Address	Service offered
Kidscape www.kidscape.org.uk	Kidscape is the only national charity dedicated to preventing bullying and child sexual abuse.
Women's Aid www.womensaid.org.uk	Offers support and a place of safety to abused women and children by providing refuges and other services.
www.thehivsupportcentre.org.uk	Confidential information, advice and support on all aspects of sexual health including HIV.
Children's Law Centre Tel: 028 90 245704	They publish a comprehensive information pack on the law relating to children and young people in Northern Ireland.

21. Personal budgets

Aims

At the end of this unit you should be able to:

- understand the relationship between income and spending
- differentiate between needs and wants
- draw up a personal budget prioritising needs and wants.

Have you ever thought about how you are going to manage your money when you begin to earn it? You may feel that you have lots of money to spend on all those things that you've always dreamed about buying. However, at some stage in your life you may have to make decisions on how you are going to manage your hard-earned income. You may have to cope with the responsibility of balancing your spending and income. This is called 'budgeting'.

Drawing up a budget will help you to make decisions:

- It will help you to plan how you are going to spend your income.
- It will help you to distinguish between needs and wants and to prioritise them.

Needs and wants

Needs can be classified as essentials that we must have in order to stay alive. Everyone needs:

- food to nurture their body
- clothes to protect their body from the cold and heat
- shelter to keep warm/dry
- services to keep them alive (e.g., medical services).

Wants can be described as types of luxuries that are not essential to everyday life but would enhance it and make it more enjoyable. Everyone has different wants depending on their own personal circumstances and experiences. Examples include:

- sports cars
- DVD players
- holidays
- air-conditioning.

Which of these are needs and which are wants?

Drawing up a budget

A budget can be described as a mathematical look into future income and expenditure. It involves a process of forward planning, either on a short-term or long-term basis. A short-term budget will have an emphasis on how you are going to manage your income for the week or month ahead, whereas a long-term budget will be concerned with planning a holiday, buying Christmas presents or splashing out on a new car. Either way, you will be analysing whether you can meet your various financial commitments.

As you only have a certain amount of money at your disposal to spend on various needs and wants it is of vital importance that your necessities are prioritised. Remember, constructing a personal budget is one thing, but keeping to it is even more important in order to prevent debt.

John's budget

Imagine the scenario of John, a 16-year-old student with a part-time job. His weekly budget would appear something like this:

INCOME	£	EXPENDITURE	£
Part-time job	30	School meals	13
Pocket money	10	CDs, magazines, etc.	7
		Weekend entertainment	15
		Savings	5
Totals:	40		40

John's spending is limited to £40 per week. He has budgeted for savings in this weekly budget, but another type of expenditure may suddenly arise that he has not foreseen and therefore his savings may have to be abandoned for this week. However, this situation may not arise until sometime in his next few weeks' budgets, giving him time to forsake his weekend entertainment to budget and save a few extra pounds. Therefore, if John cannot afford various wants or luxuries straightaway, then his budget may inevitably involve decisions on saving as well as on his intended expenditure.

In such ways, John should be prepared to change his budget quite regularly, if necessary, in order to cater for unexpected outgoings as well as unexpected but welcomed income, such as money for his birthday, etc.

activity

- Draw up a budget for yourself for next week. Remember to record all the income you will be receiving. Construct a list of your intended expenditure, prioritising your needs and wants.
- Does your spending actually balance with your income? If not, why? Where are you going to get the extra income from to balance your budget?
- Alternatively, you may have some money left over at the end of the week. You could think about saving this money for future expenditure.
- Discuss some ways you could increase your income. How do you think you would use this money to balance your budget?

22. Household budgets

Aims

At the end of this unit you should be able to:

- understand the significance of a household budget
- classify various expenditure under the headings of needs or wants
- understand the importance of balancing a household budget.

While most people are concerned with drawing up personal budgets, it is extremely important that households prepare a budget as well. In order to budget effectively, all income coming into the household, in whatever form, needs to be accounted for, such as:

- each member of the household's wage/salary
- government benefits (e.g., child benefit)
- interest from savings
- pensions
- rent from other property, etc.

The type and amount of income will obviously depend on the circumstances of each individual household.

What is a household?

A household may consist of family members who live together in the same house or a group of people sharing accommodation (e.g., students at university). Obviously the type of household budget prepared will vary according to the nature of the household arrangements.

Planning a budget

A household will try to monitor its committed expenditure and then match this to its forecasted income. This will ensure that all financial commitments are met and may cater for any unforeseen crisis.

Each household will prepare their budget according to the frequency of the majority of their income – that is, usually either according to their weekly or monthly wage.

As with a personal budget, planning is very important. As soon as the total income for the particular period of time is established, the proposed expenditure for the same period needs to be accounted for.

What incomings and outgoings does a typical household have? Can you think of any others?

Needs and wants

Needs and wants must be considered, so careful consideration must be given to what counts as essential and non-essential expenditure. Households may have some difficulty in distinguishing between these two categories.

activity

- In small groups, study the following list of items which the majority of households spend their income on. Discuss which of these you think are needs or wants. It may help you if you substitute the word 'essentials' for needs and the word 'luxuries' for wants.

Clothes	Newspaper
Newspapers	Milk
Electricity	Rent
Car insurance	Refrigerator
Council/Water rates	Computer
Furniture	Magazines
Film at cinema	Chocolate cake
Holiday	Coat
Levi jeans	Sky television
Christmas tree	Bread

- Elect a spokesperson from your group to report your results to the whole class.
- Did you find any differences between your results and those from the other groups? If so, does this relate back to the scenario that everyone may not agree on what is a 'need' or a 'want'?

Bills

It must be remembered that many household bills have to be paid on a monthly, quarterly or yearly basis, so, consequently some money needs to be set aside in the weekly or monthly budget to cater for this. When the bill arrives it may seem an enormous amount, but, if the household has prepared the budget very carefully, then the payment of this bill should not be an enormous task.

Holidays

Planning a holiday is a very important consideration in most household budgets. Careful thought and planning must be given to all expenses not only relating directly to the actual holiday, but also relating to the various expenses that may have to be incurred before the holiday even begins.

activity

Working in pairs, make a list of expenses that need to be considered before household members actually go on a holiday abroad 'in the sun'. Now divide your list into essentials and luxuries.

You need to plan well in advance to budget for a holiday.

Balancing a budget

When preparing a household budget, it is particularly important that the proposed expenditure is matched with the total income. If excess money needs to be spent then a household will either have to:

- Forego various wants. This will obviously involve considerable discussion among the members of the household.
- Increase the income coming into the household. It may be necessary for some members of the household to work extra hours.
- Contemplate borrowing money. However, it must be borne in mind that if money is borrowed there will be extra to add to the list of expenditure, with **instalments** to be repaid including added interest.

23. Household bills 1

Aims

At the end of this unit you should be able to:

- identify the various essential household bills
- distinguish the most appropriate payment period for each bill
- develop a sense of value judgement regarding each household bill.

Prioritising needs and wants is very important in the preparation of a household budget. Obviously, priority should be given to the payment of the essential household bills.

Calculating the total amount of all household bills over a period of a year should enable you to work out how much should be set aside in reserve each week or month.

Needs

Nowadays, most households have common essential household bills. Without doubt, each bill varies according to the particular household. Bills will probably include:

- food
- rent or mortgage repayments
- council/water rates
- gas
- electricity
- telephone
- house insurance
- car insurance
- car taxation
- television licence
- hire-purchase payments
- insurance premiums.

These bills will be paid at various times in the year, appropriate to the financial position of the household.

Which of these two households might have the bigger bills to pay? Why?

Value judgement

Value judgement means making a decision about a product based on quality. It can involve compromise as the product you would like is not always the one you can afford.

Value judgement is very important in successful financial management. Self-discipline is the key to effective budgeting as it is easy to be persuaded into buying something you think you need when you may not be able to afford it. This applies to essential items (e.g., food and clothes) as well as luxury items.

activity

- Right is a list of expenses which may appear in the budget for your particular household. Working in small groups at a computer, key this list into a table and indicate with a star, under the particular heading, which you think would be the most appropriate payment period for each item. The first expense has been done for you.

Mortgage	Television licence	Newspapers
Rent	Food	Gas
Council/Water rates	Car tax	Window cleaner
Electricity	House insurance	Sky television
Car fuel	Car insurance	Magazines
Hire-purchase payments	Clothes	Telephone

Expense	Daily	Weekly	Monthly	Quarterly	Yearly
Mortgage			*		

- Discuss within your group whether these items of expenditure are needs or wants.

Food

Obviously, food will be regarded as the main essential expense in almost every household. It is a basic need which keeps people alive. However, different brands or types of food cost different amounts of money; you should use value judgement to make a decision based on what you can afford rather than what you might like to afford.

Clothes

Clothes can be regarded as another basic need. With variations in the climate, it is important to purchase different types of summer and winter clothing. As with food, your level of income should undoubtedly dictate the level of expenditure on clothes. However, on most occasions the amount of money spent on clothes is usually influenced by fashion trends rather than by what people actually need in terms of clothing to protect their bodies from extreme temperatures.

Prioritising

Without doubt, the pressures of advertising tend to override money management plans with regard to many household expenses. Essential household bills should remain a vital consideration in the household budget before any other luxury expenditure is even considered.

Maintaining the habit of prioritising both wants and needs is important, even within each of the household bills. For example, this can apply to the electricity bill which could be reduced by using less electricity. The same exercise can be applied to telephone bills by making sure that the cheapest option is chosen and used for mobile phones and land-lines.

Inevitably, whether the household expense varies accordingly from week to week (e.g., for electricity or telephone bills), or remains constant for a longer period of time (e.g., the mortgage, or council or water rates bills), it must be remembered that all expenditure must be accounted for in order to budget effectively. It is therefore crucial to a household budget that expenditure patterns are considered.

You should be aware of the cost of different options.

activity

In groups, discuss how each of the following household bills could be reduced: telephone, electricity, food and clothes.

24. Household bills 2

Aims

At the end of this unit you should be able to:

- understand the layout of household bills
- calculate the total cost of an electricity bill
- understand the various methods involved in the payment of household bills.

Since the majority of household bills vary considerably according to the extent of the usage of the service, it is inevitable that it can be difficult to calculate the total bill over a period of, perhaps, a year.

The layout of most household bills are now quite easy to understand. This means that the members of the household can see at a glance how they have been charged for a particular service. A good example to look at is the electricity bill.

A household's electricity bill can arrive every three months (i.e., every quarter). Every customer has a meter which has been fitted by their electricity board. This meter is designed to keep a record of the number of electricity units used by the customer.

The electricity meter is usually read by a representative from the electricity board. Any member of a household can take the reading, if it is not possible for the representative to do so, and this 'self-reading' is shown as such on the bill.

The meter reading for each quarter is recorded and compared with the reading from the previous quarter. It is the difference between these two readings that decides the amount of a household's electricity bill.

The charge for the electricity used is priced per unit. **Value added tax** (VAT), calculated at a certain percentage according to whether it is household or business premises, is then added to the cost of the total units used.

How many items in this room affect the cost of the electricity bill when in use?

activity

Mr and Mrs Smyth have just received their electricity bill. Using the following information, calculate the total cost of their electricity bill for this quarter.

Present reading:	654311 units
Previous reading:	632477 units
The price charged for each unit is 9.55p	
VAT is charged at the rate of 5%	

Paying the electricity bill

As with most household bills, the electricity service provides payment details on the reverse of the bill, highlighting the payment methods available. Various methods are listed with a description of each. These can include:

- sending a cheque through the post
- paying at a post office counter, bank, electricity showroom, pay point or pay zone outlet
- using the **Direct Debit** service of a bank or building society
- installing a 'keypad meter', whereby customers can pay for their electricity on a 'Pay as you go' basis.

Obviously each household will discuss the various payment options on offer and decide which one best suits their personal circumstances. This will apply to the majority of all household bills.

activity

Working in groups of three, study the electricity bill shown below and answer the following questions:

- On what date did the meter reading take place?
- How many units were used during this quarter?
- What does the term 'quarterly' mean?
- How much does each unit of electricity cost?
- What does 'VAT' stand for?
- List four different methods of payment for this bill, giving a brief explanation of each method.

Helplines

Customer helplines for the various utilities are available to give customers advice on how to pay their bills, as well as how to make efficient use of their particular service. For example, Northern Ireland Electricity publish 'Codes of Practice for people with disabilities as well as the elderly in our society'. British Telecommunications offer assistance through contact by telephone, fax, e-mail and access to their website.

SAVE MONEY ON YOUR GAS BILL - PHONE FREE ON 0800 978576 356475

synergy
Energy For Life

ELECTRICITY BILL 0344 568435 987
Thank you for using our service
Your bill is now due for payment
If you have any queries, or need help

Please phone us free on 0800 19746586 and quote your customer number

Date of Issue 12 Jan 2004

MR. WACKFORD SQUEERS
Dodgy Boys Academy
Orpington
Kent OT1 8UR

Meter readings (E = Estimate C = Your own) This time	Last time	Units used	Pence per unit	Amount £
Domestic Household Tariff 31828E	312032E	796	6.410	51.02
Standing charge up to 10 Jan 2004		97 days at	9.40	9.12
Total charges this quarter excl. VAT				
VAT 5% on				3.00
Total charges this quarter incl. VAT			60.14	63.14
				TOTAL NOW DUE £63.14

An electricity bill.

25. Financial problems

Aims

At the end of this unit you should be able to:

- understand the implications of impulse buying
- identify the factors influencing unplanned purchases
- realise the consequences of not adhering to a budget.

Keeping to a budget

The reason for preparing a budget, whether a personal budget or a household budget, is to ensure that you have peace of mind that you can afford to pay for essentials, as well as most of your wants. Although you might have spent many long hours calculating and discussing with other members of your household how you could balance your income and expenditure, your initial planning of the budget is only the beginning. Keeping to the budget makes it all worthwhile. For most people this can be very difficult. If you fail to keep to the set budget, you have to bear the consequences.

activity

Prepare a talk (three–four minutes) on the following scenario and present it to your class in order to generate a class discussion. Consider the following points:

- Think about the last time you failed to keep to your personal budget.
- How did you feel?
- What circumstances caused you to stray from your budget?
- Did you feel that perhaps you might have been too strict on yourself when trying to match your income with your expenditure?
- Did you allow for every type of expenditure in your budget?
- Did you prepare a revised budget for yourself in the light of what happened?

Impulse buying

Obviously, some attractive outside influences can have a very negative effect on your budget. You need to be on your guard against the pressures of the media regarding persuasive advertising and fashion trends.

If you succumb to the temptation of making an unplanned luxury purchase, as most people do at some stage, the defined expenditure in your budget becomes meaningless and your carefully planned, prioritised list is foolishly abandoned.

Impulse buying is hard to resist.

The tendency to impulse buy will have a detrimental effect on a personal budget, but any form of unplanned spending will seriously affect a household budget. All members of a household will suffer financially if just one member buys an expensive item on impulse.

Major financial decisions will have to be discussed regarding further planning of the household budget. Balancing income with expenditure will now become more cumbersome, as the level of expenditure will have risen considerably with the unplanned spending. The previously prioritised list will need to be re-examined and other planned purchases may have to be foregone in order to maintain some level of balance in the household budget.

On the other hand, the household may be able to raise its level of income for a period of time, with extra revenue sought through part-time work or other various fund-raising activities. The household may even have the 'ideal budget' in which an extra amount of money had been built, just in case. Obviously, this well-planned extra amount would only be drawn upon in an emergency.

Needless to say, unless the above strategies are applied when impulse buying occurs the household will be faced with a DEBT. All their carefully thought-out plans will no longer be applicable and their planned luxuries may become a non-reality. Their budget will have lost its impact and the household may not know which way to turn.

activity

- Working in pairs, make a list of various items which you bought on impulse over the past few weeks.
- What effect did these unplanned purchases have on your personal budget?
- Why do you think you purchased these items?
- Discuss how the following factors would have influenced your purchases:
  - peer-group pressure
  - fashion-trends
  - items attractively displayed in prominent positions in retail outlets
  - it seemed like a good bargain at the time
  - boredom.
- Can you think of any other factors that may have persuaded you to purchase on impulse?
- Compare your findings with other groups in the class. Did you have any common impulse purchases?
- Discuss the influential factors relating to these purchases that were common to most groups.

Would you be able to decide which way to go if you had a cash-flow problem?

26. Debt

Aims

At the end of this unit you should be able to:

- understand the meaning of the word 'debt'
- examine the issues relating to a **mortgage**.

Have you ever been in the position where you have borrowed money from your parents, your brothers or sisters, or even your friends, to make a purchase that you didn't have the money for? If so, then you have placed yourself in debt in order to pay for something that you couldn't afford.

activity

- In groups of four, make a list of all the people that you have borrowed money from, mentioning the reasons why you borrowed the money. Some of the following excuses for borrowing money may jog your memory:
  - to pay for a school dinner on a Friday
  - to buy a newly released CD before your other friends were able to buy it
  - to pay off the remainder of a school trip before the deadline
  - to complete the payment on a new football-team jersey
  - to attend the last disco before returning to school after the holidays.
- Did you later pay back any of the money that you borrowed? If not, why not?
- If you did not pay back the money you borrowed then you are actually still in debt to your lenders. How do you feel about this?
- Now report your group's findings to the class.

More than likely, the amounts you have borrowed until now have only been small. Your parents or other members of your family will probably not expect you to pay them back, as they realise that you only have a limited amount of income through, perhaps, a part-time job.

However, you must realise that as you become older, your commitments and wants may not be satisfied through your income, so, therefore, you will need to seek financial help from somewhere else. Your parents and other members of your family will have their own ideas for their hard-earned income, so you will obviously have to access funds from various outside agencies in order to purchase items that you cannot afford to pay for yourself. In reality, you will be putting yourself in debt.

Think hard before you put yourself in debt.

activity

- Debate the following motion in groups: 'If you cannot afford to purchase an item, should you put yourself into debt to do so?'
- Decide whether you are in favour of this motion or against it. Prepare a five-minute report and present it to the class.

Mortgages

Some people loathe the idea of getting into debt and prefer to save for an item before purchasing it. However, even the most economical and prudent earner will realise that one basic need, namely a home, would take quite a considerable number of years' savings to purchase outright. Consequently, it is worthwhile considering the option of borrowing money in this instance. It could prove to be a very sensible decision in the years ahead.

The actual term given to this type of borrowing is 'mortgage'. This loan from a bank or building society will commit you to repayment arrangements stretching over a number of years.

The decision to obtain a mortgage should not be taken lightly. Various factors need to be taken into consideration regarding a household budget before this long-term financial commitment can be undertaken. A great deal of consultation and discussion is of paramount importance addressing the following issues:

- the actual amount of loan required to buy the house, including the ability to provide the deposit or part of it
- the feasibility of the repayment time (the age of the borrower is significant here)
- the fluctuation of interest rates
- the actual type of mortgage sought (e.g., endowment or repayment)
- the effect of the repayments on the household budget (this is the most important issue to be considered).

activity

Why do you think this last issue is of such importance? In small groups discuss the implications of this issue.

While it may seem to be beneficial to borrow money in order to obtain something that you wish to have immediately, it is absolutely vital that you weigh up these benefits against the cost of borrowing in the long term. With mortgages, as indeed with any form of credit, it must be remembered that these repayments will have a serious effect on expenditure in your household budget. If you cannot afford to maintain your repayments you will find yourself in a vicious circle of debt.

Think carefully before committing yourself to a mortgage.

27. Borrowing money

Aims

At the end of this unit you should be able to:

- identify and understand various ways of borrowing money.

There are various ways of borrowing money, for purchases that are unbudgeted for, or for large purchases that people cannot afford to buy outright.

Credit

Credit is the term used to describe the acquisition of goods or services without actually paying for them there and then, or paying for them using someone else's money.

Credit facilitators

Finance-lending agencies such as banks, building societies, credit unions and finance houses offer attractive rates of borrowing on their loans, overdrafts, mortgages, budget accounts, etc. Key issues need to be addressed regarding the choice of the most appropriate method of borrowing from each of these financial institutions. Some of these could include:

- the actual purpose for which the amount borrowed is needed
- the period within which the amount needs to be repaid
- the rate of interest charged on the borrowed amount
- the possibility of extending the repayment period in the eventuality of an unforeseen crisis.

All types of credit agreements must, by law, promote truth in relation to **annual percentage rates (APR)** and credit terms offered, in order that the consumer can effectively compare the costs of the different forms of credit.

Read all literature carefully.

activity

Key the terms and brief definitions into your computer as they appear in this table. Using the cut and paste facility, match each term to its correct definition. Now print a copy of your work.

INTEREST	A loan to buy property
REPAYMENT PERIOD	A method of purchasing goods, spreading payments over a period of time
MORTGAGE	An amount incurred as a result of the use of credit or borrowed money
CREDIT SALE	Percentage charged for borrowing
OVERDRAFT	A period of time over which an amount of money is repaid
INTEREST RATE	The facility to draw on extra funds in your current account

Credit, debit and in-store cards

The increasing use of technology has dramatic effects on everyday financial transactions. Obtaining credit has become a significantly painless exercise for all age groups. Greater emphasis is being placed on a diminishing need for 'cash up front'.

As a result, the 'plastic card' is rapidly replacing the traditional notes and coins as a form of payment. Some consumers have welcomed this transition, indicating the attractive convenience with all forms of credit purchases, using a variety of credit, debit and in-store cards. However, interest rates and credit limits vary according to the nature of these cards, so consumers must closely examine the implications of each in relation to their own particular circumstances.

The Internet

The development of **e-commerce** and the World Wide Web has had a major effect on consumer shopping habits and, consequently, on financial management. Research is beginning to reveal that more and more consumers are 'surfing the Net' in order to identify the cheapest supplier and the cheapest prices.

It only takes a few minutes to buy on-line and pay by credit card. However, the convenience of such shopping may tempt consumers further into the 'credit trap' – that is, continually purchasing goods on credit – and, ultimately, further into debt.

You could save money by 'surfing the Net'.

activities

1. Have you ever purchased something using the Internet? If so, what type of purchase was it? How did you pay for it?
2. Find out the names of credit cards used by members of your family. List the type of purchases they use them for. Compare your findings with other class members.
3. Read these two different viewpoints concerning the idea of buying on credit:
   - Some people are of the opinion that credit is a very favourable tool as it helps them to obtain goods and services that they would not otherwise be able to afford for quite a considerable time.
   - Other people believe that credit can cause serious debt problems.

   Which of these viewpoints do you agree with? Prepare a five-minute presentation to share your views with the rest of the class.

28. Credit

Aims

At the end of this unit you should be able to:

- understand the significance of credit.

Nowadays, very few people live their lives without using some form of credit. Using such services as electricity or the telephone and then making payments when the bill arrives is a method of obtaining services on credit.

Buying on credit

Consumer credit is part and parcel of everyday life. This technological age has an effect on people's financial commitments. People are continually drawn into situations where there is always something new and updated to buy. Wants become insatiable and sometimes people's incomes can't keep up. More often than not, people succumb to the temptation of 'buying now and paying later'.

Sometimes it can prove to be more financially worthwhile to improve personal standard of living by opting for this scenario of paying for goods and services at a later date. Purchasing a luxury item on credit can ultimately mean that people still have funds at their disposal to facilitate the purchase of an essential item which is crucial to their everyday needs.

Interest-free

It is even more beneficial to purchase goods on an interest-free credit basis, whereby interest charges are not added to the overall cost. On occasions such as this, it would seem to make more financial sense to buy on credit (especially if the item in question costs less than it will by the time enough money has been saved to pay for it).

activity

- Using newspapers and magazines, cut out advertisements for goods on which interest-free credit is offered.
- Working in small groups, produce a collage depicting the items offered with this method of credit.
- Have a class discussion on the type of products where consumer credit is offered. Are you really getting value for money in the long term?

Interest

It may not always be possible to buy all non-affordable goods on an interest-free credit basis; therefore, you must realise that credit purchases will inevitably cost more money as they incur an interest charge. For example, something that costs £200 to buy outright might end up costing £250 if bought on credit, because of the interest charges.

There is a lot of competition inviting people to borrow money or to buy things on credit. With credit facilities so readily available and convenient, many people can unwittingly become 'trapped' by borrowing money they can't afford to repay. All too often, people are tempted by the persuasive credit offers that seem almost too good to be true. They therefore find themselves in debt, in a way that is practically impossible to escape from.

Society is becoming more and more 'cashless'. Are notes and coins going out of fashion?

activity

Design an A4 poster, advertising credit facilities for the purchase of a suite of furniture. Use various font styles, colours, borders and shadings as well as clip-art and word-art to illustrate your advert.

Shopping around

When was the last time you purchased a fairly expensive item? Did you compare its price in more than one shop? If so, what were your reasons for doing this, in relation to your personal budget?

On the other hand you may have received money as a birthday present and felt you had no need to shop around. Do you think you were justified in making this decision? If you had shopped around, what effect would this decision have made on your personal budget?

Since you are still a student, you will no doubt value your income, whether you earn it through a part-time job or receive it as a means of pocket money from your parents. Either way, you will obviously exercise some form of prudence when you are spending it. If you realise that you can obtain a cheaper purchase in a certain retail outlet as opposed to another, then you will no doubt purchase the item at the cheaper price.

This type of shopping around should also apply to choosing where you borrow money from.

It would take a long time to save money and buy the items above outright.

Credit sales

Most people think that if they shop around for a good deal when purchasing an item – either essential or luxury – and paying for it outright, they feel a sense of achievement when parting with their hard-earned money. The same feeling can be applied to a credit sale. The whole idea of borrowing money or buying goods and services on credit must be carefully considered in relation to good overall financial management.

Financial institutions and credit facilitators are all too willing to lend you money. When deciding to borrow money, paying it back must be accounted for in your budget. It is therefore of the utmost importance that you borrow sensibly, and choose the right form of credit, otherwise problems with escalating debts will follow.

29. Renting or buying property

Aims

At the end of this unit you should be able to:

- explore financial options such as renting property as opposed to buying it.

At some stage in your life there will come a time when you would like to have your own independence and set up a home of your own. Some of you may experience this situation sooner than others. Perhaps in a few years' time you might go to university and not want to travel a long way every day. Therefore, it will be necessary to look for alternative living accommodation for the length of time you are there.

You may decide that it is time to move out of the family home. Perhaps you may decide to get married and start sharing a home with your spouse.

There are two basic alternatives:

1. renting accommodation
2. buying a home.

Both of these options carry benefits and constraints and what may be suitable for one person may be unsuitable for another.

The choice of whether to rent or buy accommodation will depend on various factors, including:

- your financial management plan (i.e., how affordable a mortgage would be at a particular time in your life)
- whether you want a long-term commitment
- the state of the housing market
- fluctuation in interest rates
- the amount of legal fees and expenses incurred when buying a house.

Rent or buy – the choice is yours.

Renting property

In most areas, various types of accommodation are available for renting and the type chosen will depend on the needs of the individual. Houses, flats and apartments are among the main types of rented accommodation. Students or work-mates usually rent these properties and pay their share of the rent. However, there are other options, such as:

- renting a room in a house through a landlord or landlady where you might receive cooked meals
- accommodation in a hostel.

As previously stated, any type of rented property has benefits as well as drawbacks. Some of the benefits may include:

- the amount of money needed for a deposit is smaller when renting, although advance rent for a period of time may be requested as well
- there is the possibility of short-term renting with an agreement of a period of notice
- the cost of rent may not fluctuate as much as mortgage repayments
- the major up-keep costs are usually the responsibility of the owner.

The disadvantages of renting will also need to be considered before any decisions are made regarding a home. They include:

- the property will not become your own while you rent it
- having the period of notice means that you may have to look for alternative accommodation if the owner wants you to leave
- the owner may impose various restrictions regarding renovations and decoration.

activity

- Bring in local newspapers from home and look at the adverts relating to houses or flats for rent.
- Imagine you are 18 years old and seeking a place of your own. Which of these properties would suit your requirements?
- Prepare a three-minute talk on your choice of property, giving reasons for your decision, and present it to the class.

Buying your own home

Shop around for the best mortgage deal.

Buying your own home will probably provide you with that little extra independence and self-esteem. The benefits can be summed up as follows:

- making mortgage repayments will ensure that the property eventually belongs to you
- selling the property for more than the purchase price could give you a healthy profit
- making improvements to the house will usually increase the value of the property, therefore making it a worthy future investment.

Failure to keep paying your mortgage repayments may lead to you losing your home, which is a major drawback when purchasing property. Other constraints include:

- the value of the property may decrease, resulting in mortgage repayments being more than the property is worth
- there may be a rise in interest rates, which would affect your mortgage repayments
- a percentage of the mortgage must be paid as a deposit on top of your legal fees and expenses.

In order to come to a decision about whether to rent or buy, you will need to be aware of the various implications involved in both of these options.

activity

Sean and Mary are getting married in the near future. They cannot decide whether to rent or buy their first home. With one of your class friends, prepare a five-minute dialogue exploring both options before reaching a suitable decision.

30. Second-hand versus new

Aims

At the end of this unit you should be able to:

- explore the purchasing options of second-hand versus new.

Value for money

Getting value for money does wonders for your self-esteem. Everyone strives to purchase wisely in order to achieve the best possible satisfaction from their purchases. People continually find themselves making decisions when purchasing goods and services, but, inevitably, their individual planned budgets dictate their items of expenditure.

In reality income has a major effect on people's purchases and influences their spending power; their choices will be determined by responsibility – the responsibility to spend their money wisely.

You might recognise the phrase 'making money stretch'. This means purchasing as much as possible in relation to how much you can spend. Obtaining value for money involves recognising what you can and cannot afford in relation to your financial circumstances.

Financial management ensures economical use of money. Consequently, people find themselves considering buying second-hand, as opposed to buying new.

activity

A number of people will go through life without ever contemplating the idea of buying second-hand goods. In groups of four, discuss reasons why you think this happens. Now compare the outcome of your discussion with other groups in the class.

Affordability is a major factor in the choice between new and second-hand purchases. Some people may have such a high income that they do not need to consider this option. Other consumers may want their income to stretch as far as possible and if this means buying second-hand, then so be it.

activities

1. Make a list of items that you have bought second-hand at some stage in your life (these could include items bought from friends, once they have finished with them, e.g., a CD, DVD, bicycle, golf-equipment, a computer game, etc.).
2. It is likely that circumstances relating to your personal budget influenced your decision to buy second-hand goods. How did you feel about purchasing these items second-hand? Did it help your self-esteem in that you felt you were getting good value for money? Share your thoughts with other members of the class.

Second-hand purchases

Purchasing second-hand items does not mean that we are losing quality. Naturally the item will have been used by the previous owner, but this does not necessarily mean you are getting poor quality. If you find that you can make a more economical purchase within your budget, then you are adopting a responsible attitude towards your financial management. After all, the key to successful budgeting is sensible decision-making, regarding all types of expenditure.

The brand new car loses a large percentage of its value as soon as it leaves the showroom. Which purchase is therefore the better buy?

Payment

It must be remembered that purchasing an item new, as opposed to second-hand, will provide greater payment method choices (e.g., credit or **hire-purchase**). Most second-hand products are sold on a 'cash only' basis. 'Buy now and pay later' is often the motto regarding durable goods; when this is available, it can be the deciding factor between buying new or second-hand.

Guarantees

You should be aware that service contracts and guarantees may not be included when purchasing second-hand goods. It is worth considering whether these 'offers' are beneficial to your individual needs before you actually commit to a purchase. Obviously you will have to weigh up the benefits and constraints of purchasing items without warranty deals as it could prove more expensive and demanding on your budget if the second-hand item fails to operate perfectly.

If you are seeking purchases with the most modern and up-to-date features, you will be swayed towards the new version of the item. The increasing use of technology in all areas of production has ensured continual innovation in the manufacture of all consumer goods.

activity

Using a computer, make a list of six personal items that you have owned for quite some time (e.g., a mobile phone, CD player, etc.) and mention features on each that are different in newer models. Present your work in the form of a table as in the example.

Personal items	Features
Mobile phone	
CD player	

Now discuss with the other members of your class whether you would be prepared to actually buy these items second-hand nowadays. What would influence your decision?

31. Dealing with debt

Aims

At the end of this unit you should be able to:

- understand how to deal with debt.

With careful financial planning and a cautious attitude towards credit purchases, you should have every avenue explored regarding the income and expenditure of your personal or household budget. In reality, however, unforeseen problems can occur (e.g., being made redundant or becoming ill) which may lead to situations where repayments on credit purchases cannot be met. In such situations, you will end up in debt; how you deal with this debt is most important. Your actions can either have a positive or negative effect on an already critical situation.

What doors are open to us if we get into debt?

Remember, debt will not go away on its own! If you try to ignore the problem you could find yourself facing a court prosecution for non-payment.

If you run into difficulty with repayments, it is essential to sit down and take account of the whole situation as soon as possible. You should re-examine your budget and carefully consider if you can either increase your source of income or decrease your expenditure. You may require some financial guidance in order to help steer your budget back onto the right track.

See if you can negotiate repayments.

Seek help

Initially it is a good idea to contact the organisation that granted you credit. They may offer an alternative repayment plan (e.g., reschedule a loan, which may reduce the immediate debt situation). It will mean that you will end up paying more than you anticipated, as you will run up more interest on the original amount borrowed. It is important that you keep to this revised payment schedule in order to avoid a similar situation arising in the near future.

activity

Alan has just discovered that his bills have been mounting up and he realises that he is going to end up in serious debt if he cannot find a solution. He borrowed £3,000 from his local credit union to help him purchase a car and now he feels that he needs to contact the manageress and explain that he is finding it difficult to keep up his repayments. He would be very willing to re-negotiate his repayment terms.

Using this scenario, perform a five-minute role play of the above situation, with one student acting the part of Alan and another student playing the part of the credit union manageress.

Family and friends

It can be an unwise decision to borrow money to pay off your debts. In most cases it could increase your debt problems. However, there may be exceptions to this. Members of your family or close friends may be able to lend you money, without having to pay any interest. No doubt, this loan will help you to reduce your immediate debt to creditors but don't forget that you will still be in debt to your family or friends and will need to take account of this extra borrowing in your personal or household budget.

Shop around

If you are unable to borrow money from close acquaintances then it may be worthwhile to approach a financial institution (e.g., a bank or building society) that offers lower interest rates. This could apply to a credit card debt and might help to alleviate the debt problem in the short term.

Free advice

Your local Citizens Advice Bureau is always an available source for advice on financial matters. They provide free advice to all members of the public about a number of issues including the payment of debt. They will probably also advise you to contact your local Social Security Office to check whether you are entitled to claim any benefits.

You need to be very careful in your choice of assistance when you have a debt problem. Unfortunately, many people turn immediately to pawnbrokers and loan-sharks that usually charge exceedingly high rates of interest for borrowing and force them into even more debt.

It is worth remembering that if your debts remain unpaid to a credit company your 'credit rating' may be affected, with the result that you could possibly be refused credit sometime in the future.

activity

Jenny has just received her credit card statement. She has realised that she has overspent her budget over the past month and may be unable to repay her credit card company. She discusses the problem with her friend Marie. What advice do you think Marie should give to help her solve her credit card debt problem?

32. Consumer protection

Aims

At the end of this unit you should be able to:

- know the rights of the consumer
- understand the relevant consumer protection legislation.

Goods and services that we purchase must meet certain standards. Modern-day advertisements, coupled with the high-profile manner in which goods and services are marketed, can be very persuasive in such a way that you, as a consumer, could make an incorrect purchasing decision. It is easy to be misled, so it is important that you help protect yourself by purchasing carefully. There is always a need for the 'buyer to be aware' when purchasing any type of goods or service.

Having purchased products, the consumer is responsible for exercising care and attention when using the particular product. Printed instructions by the manufacturer should be carefully read and carried out accordingly.

If you find fault with your purchase, you should contact the seller as soon as possible. Buyers should not be intimidated by sellers trying to escape from their legal responsibilities. The law implies that sellers should endeavour to deal with complaints about faulty goods rather than laying the blame at the manufacturer's door.

Consumer law

Consumers need to be protected against businesses that advertise and sell their products and services through misleading or false descriptions of their products. Government legislation and various government agencies protect consumers and guide the entrepreneur and, ultimately, the seller in a variety of ways. The main Acts protecting the consumer are described here.

1. The Sale and Supply of Goods and Services Act 1994

This Act aims to protect you in such a way that all goods and services purchased are of satisfactory quality. The seller must ensure that the goods are:

- 'properly and safely manufactured and of a satisfactory quality'. This means that goods must be free from faults and manufactured so that they comply with safety regulations. A new item must not be damaged and should work properly.
- 'as they are described on the packaging'. This ensures that the goods correspond with the seller's actual description of them, or in accordance with the sales literature and labelling on the package.
- 'fit for the purpose for which they are sold'. If you purchase a water-resistant watch, you must actually be able to wear it in the swimming pool without damaging it.

Having purchased goods and discovered that they have not met the above criteria, you are within your rights to return the goods to the seller for a full refund.

The Trade Descriptions Act

This Act protects you from businesses that falsely describe their goods or services offered, either verbally or through written descriptions.

Weights and Measures (N. Ireland) Order 1981

This Order tries to ensure that you receive the exact quantity of a product that you believe you are actually purchasing. This makes it an offence to sell goods which do not correspond to the actual weight or measurement printed on the packaging. Weighing scales used by businesses must be totally accurate.

Consumer Protection Act 1987

This Act is twofold. It aims to protect you regarding the safety of products purchased by making it an offence to sell goods which turn out to be unsafe. The Act also safeguards you against purchasing goods on 'special offer' which turn out to be false, and against misleading prices for goods, services, accommodation or facilities.

Consumer Credit Act 1974

The purpose of this Act is to ensure that you are made aware of the true APR when you accept hire-purchase or credit sales agreements when purchasing goods or borrowing money in the form of personal credit agreements. This then ensures that you can make realistic comparisons between the various credit facilities offered by sellers.

activity

Working in pairs, read the scenarios below. Decide which Act they apply to and how the particular Act has been broken. Discuss what action should be taken in each case.

- Pete was chosen as a runner for his local athletic team. He bought a new pair of trainers but after wearing them for a week the soles separated from the uppers.

- John and his wife Lucy decided to have a barbecue. They bought a box of burgers which stated on the outside that it contained 50 burgers. When they arrived home the box only contained 40 burgers.

- Sue purchased a jumper which stated on the label that it could be machine-washed. However, when she washed it she discovered that it had shrunk and no longer fitted her.

Glossary

Abstinence The decision not to have sex.

Adolescent Someone going through a period of change/development from childhood to adulthood.

AIDS (Acquired Immune Deficiency Syndrome) A series of serious illnesses that occur as a result of having HIV in your system.

Angina Disease of the heart.

Annual percentage rates (APR) The 'true' rate of interest paid on loans.

Anxiety Worry or fear of what might happen.

Balanced diet A variety of foods providing all the required nutrients to maintain your health.

Bisexual A person who is attracted to and has sexual relationships with both men and women.

Body language The messages portrayed by facial expressions, hand gestures and body posture. It is non-verbal communication.

Celibate When a person does not have any sexual activity with other people.

Conception When an egg is fertilised by a sperm cell.

Confusion Feeling mixed up.

Contraception The methods used to prevent pregnancy.

Dementia Mental deterioration usually in old people.

Dependence The compulsion to continue to take a drug in order to feel good or avoid feeling bad (dependence can be physical and psychological).

Depression Increased level of sadness or feeling low in spirit.

Diet The foods we choose to eat.

Direct Debit A method of payment, whereby a customer instructs their bank to make regular payments on their behalf to a creditor.

ECHR (European Convention on Human Rights) A convention, originally formulated in 1950, aimed at protecting the human rights of all people in the member states of the council of Europe. The convention, together with a number of subsequent protocols, defines the freedoms that each member state must guarantee to all within its jurisdiction.

E-commerce (Electronic-commerce) Availing of an on-line source to purchase goods and services on the Internet.

Fitness The ability of the body to cope with the everyday demands of life.

Gay man A man who is attracted to and has sexual relationships with other men.

Hallucination The experience of seeing something that is not really there.

Health Complete state of physical, mental and social well-being (not simply the absence of disease or infirmity).

Heterosexual A person who is attracted to and has sexual relationships with members of the opposite sex.

Hire-purchase A method of buying on credit where the purchaser pays a proportion of the cost as a deposit and pays the balance in agreed equal instalments over a period of time.

HIV (Human Immunodeficiency Virus) A virus that damages the body's immune system.

Homosexual A person who is attracted to and has sexual relationships with members of the same sex.

Hormones Chemicals made in the body that control development and change.

Instalments Fixed monthly payments on credit purchases.

Lesbian A woman who is attracted to and has sexual relationships with other women.

Media The means by which information is communicated to us (e.g., newspapers).

Mental health Our ability to cope with stress including the way we control our emotions and our feelings of self-worth.

Mortgage A loan by a financial institution to buy property.

Overdose The use of any drug in such quantities that it causes acute physical or mental problems or effects.

Peer group A social group of friends or individuals of approximately the same age or profession.

Peer influence The effect a group of peers can have on your decisions.

Peer pressure Pressure or influences put on you by your group of friends/acquaintances of your age in order to conform to their set of norms.

Personality The distinctive characteristics of a person that makes them unique.

Rape To have sexual intercourse with someone without their consent.

Self-confidence Believing in yourself and your abilities so that you can try out new experiences and be able to deal positively with setbacks.

Self-esteem Having a good opinion of yourself, knowing what your strengths are and valuing yourself as a person.

Self-image How you see yourself.

Self-respect Having a set of values and trying to live your life by them.

Sexual assault A sudden attack of a sexual nature.

Sexual harassment Unwelcome behaviour of a sexual nature.

Sexuality The feelings we have about being male or female that control our sexual behaviour, our identity, and our sexual attraction towards others.

Stereotype Making an assumption or judging someone on the basis of the group they belong to, often in an insulting way.

STIs (Sexually transmitted infections) Infections passed from one person to another through sexual contact.

Tolerance The body becomes used to a drug requiring the taker to use higher doses to get the same effect.

Transsexual A person who strongly feels that they were born in the body of one sex but have the mind of the other sex.

Value added tax (VAT) An indirect tax in the form of a percentage on the value added to goods or services.

Withdrawal The body's reaction to the sudden absence of a drug which it has become used to.

Index